D0236480

UNI

c17'

CA

METHUEN'S MONOGRAPHS
ON CHEMICAL SUBJECTS

————

General Editors: H. J. EMELÉUS, F.R.S.
D. W. G. STYLE, and R. P. BELL, F.R.S.

MECHANISMS OF OXIDATION
OF ORGANIC COMPOUNDS

MECHANISMS OF OXIDATION
OF ORGANIC COMPOUNDS

W. A. Waters
M.A., Sc.D., F.R.S.
Fellow of Balliol College, Oxford
Reader in Physical Organic Chemistry, Oxford University

LONDON: METHUEN & CO LTD
NEW YORK: JOHN WILEY & SONS INC

547.23   W

First published in Great Britain in 1964
© W. A. Waters, 1964
Printed in Great Britain by
Spottiswoode Ballantyne & Co Ltd
London & Colchester

UNIV. COLL. OF
LIBRARY
S. WALES & MON.
CARDIFF

BG404568

Contents

Preface

The study of mechanisms of oxidation of organic compounds has interested me for several years and I consider it to be a subject of major importance to all chemists, for not only does it require consideration of the properties and reactions of both organic and inorganic compounds, but, above all, it has vast implications in connection with the understanding of the nature of life.

Most of our detailed experimental information concerning the mechanisms of oxidation processes has been forthcoming only in the past 20 years, during which new facts and new views have emerged rapidly, and to many chemists knowledge of oxidation processes still may seem to require mastery of several sets of unrelated facts. In this short monograph I have attempted to view the oxidation of organic compounds as a single subject, selecting examples of reagents and reactions so as to reveal the salient electronic, structural and stereochemical features that are common to all oxidative processes.

It has not been possible to cite all the literature references that a specialist reader might wish to find, but most original sources can easily be traced by use of the General Reading References given at the conclusion of particular chapters.

Balliol College   W. A. WATERS
Oxford, May, 1963

CHAPTER 1

The Nature of Oxidation

Living organisms are all chemically reacting systems depending on the continuance of oxidations and reductions, for plants proliferate by using radiant energy to reduce carbon dioxide whilst animals obtain their vital energy by the oxidation of carbon compounds. Thus the comprehension of mechanisms of oxidation and reduction processes is essential to the understanding of the nature of life and it is a task for the organic chemist to provide a clear picture of ways in which these chemical changes may take place with simple molecules, so that biologists can have a sure basis for their understanding of the behaviour of complex organisms.

Only a brief survey of oxidation reactions of organic compounds can be given in this monograph, which therefore deals only with reactions that occur in homogeneous liquid systems. Again, space does not permit mention of experimental details which are often critically important for the successful operation of any chemical reaction.

Nearly all oxidizing agents are inorganic compounds; they contain elements that may belong to nearly all parts of the periodic classification, but fortunately theories of organic chemistry have been developed so rationally that it is a much simpler task to elucidate oxidation mechanisms in terms of modes of degradation of molecules of distinctive types than to consider separately each available oxidizing agent. This approach is used in the following chapters, each of which has to be perforce selective.

Oxidation levels of organic compounds

For practical purposes organic chemists still define oxidation and reduction in nineteenth-century terms, viz. that oxidation corresponds to gain of oxygen or loss of hydrogen. When considering organic compounds it is often helpful to assess the *oxidation level* of any molecule, or group, by reference to the successive steps of the oxidation of methane – CH_4, $CH_3.OH$, CH_2O, $H.CO_2H$, CO_2 – making the rational assumption that hydrolysis at a carbon centre, or the addition or elimination of the elements of water, involve neither oxidation nor reduction. In this way one can classify both (1) and (2) as oxidations:

1. $$CH_4 + Cl_2 \longrightarrow CH_3 . Cl + HCl$$

2. $$C_2H_4 + Br_2 \longrightarrow Br . CH_2 . CH_2 . Br$$

for $CH_3 . Cl$ has the oxidation level of $CH_3 . OH$ and $C_2H_4Br_2$ that of $C_2H_4(OH)_2$, ethylene itself corresponding to C_2H_5OH, or $2CH_3 . OH$, and thus being a more oxidized compound than C_2H_6 ($CH_3 . OH + CH_4$). In contrast, (3) is a reduction, whilst an ionization, (4), is neither an oxidation nor a reduction.

3. $$CH_3 . Cl + Mg \longrightarrow CH_3 . Mg . Cl$$

4. $$CH_3 . CO . O . H \rightleftharpoons CH_3 . CO . O^- + H^+$$

Again a carbohydrate, $C_6H_{12}O_6$ and benzene, C_6H_6, have the same oxidation level.

The electronic nature of oxidation
To the inorganic chemist the statement that oxidation is equivalent to electron loss and reduction to electron gain, e.g.

5. $$Fe^{2+} \underset{\text{Reduction}}{\overset{\text{Oxidation}}{\rightleftharpoons}} Fe^{3+} + e$$

is adequate for describing reactions of ionizable substances. By developing this concept, physical chemists compare the oxidizing powers of different ions by reference to *redox potentials*, which are measures of free energy changes in thermodynamically reversible equilibria, but often have unwarrantably been calculated from enthalpy data for irreversible reactions.

These concepts, however, are not so clearly applicable in organic chemistry, for when carbon compounds are oxidized their component atoms are very seldom deprived of their surrounding complete electron shells. Again, few oxidations of organic compounds are reversible reactions and the formulation of a reaction scheme that would lead to an overall free energy decrease gives no warranty that such a reaction can be effected. However a surprising number of oxidations and reductions which are quite unknown in a chemical laboratory can be effected by enzyme systems and all these are thermodynamically reversible.

It is instructive, however, to examine the movements of valency electrons that occur in any simple oxidation such as (1) above. From the oxidation level viewpoint it can be said that CH_3—Cl is in a more oxidized state than CH_4, but by considering these molecules only it would be difficult to assert that electrons had been removed from methane on its conversion to methyl chloride. However, each chemical reaction should be considered as a whole, without making a special selection of one reactant and one reaction product, and when this is done electron counting reveals that two chlorine atoms are initially associated, in Cl_2, with 14 valency electrons and eventually, in CH_3—Cl + HCl, with 16. Clearly chlorine has been reduced and therefore methane has been oxidized; two electrons have in fact been abstracted with the hydrogen nucleus that has been replaced by chlorine.

In the hydrolysis (6)

6. $$CH_3\text{—}Cl + OH^- \longrightarrow CH_3\text{—}OH + Cl^-$$

electron transfer occurs, but there is no overall electron loss or gain by any reaction product, for Cl^- possesses exactly the same number of valency electrons as OH^-.

Classification of oxidation processes

As explained above, the study of oxidation is essentially an examination of ways by which electrons can be removed from organic compounds. Now organic compounds are essentially covalent and have their valency electrons associated together in pairs. Moreover they are mainly composed of a carbon skeleton surrounded by a skin of hydrogen and consequently have few superficial electrons accessible for direct attack by colliding reagents. Covalent bond fission is an essential feature of organic reactions and it can be effected by two different pathways, viz. *homolytic reactions* in which electron pairs are symmetrically disrupted and *heterolytic reactions* in which electron pairs are transferred from one particle to another as an undivided entity. Electron removals by these two pathways have clearly distinguishable characteristics.

In *homolytic oxidations* electrons are removed singly from organic molecules by active atoms, such as chlorine, or by active free radicals. Though molecules containing unshared electrons can be oxidized in this way, homolytic oxidations usually involve the removal from an organic molecule of one electron together with a hydrogen nucleus, e.g.

7. $$R_3C\text{—}H + \cdot Cl \longrightarrow R_3C\cdot + H\text{—}Cl$$

The initial organic product necessarily has an unpaired electron and so must perforce undergo a reaction of similar type, e.g.

8. $R_3C\cdot + Cl\!-\!Cl \longrightarrow R_3C\!-\!Cl + \cdot Cl$

or must combine with another free radical before stable entities alone result. Thus chain reactions, dimerizations or disproportionations, e.g.

9. $2C_2H_5\cdot \longrightarrow C_2H_6 + C_2H_4$

are typical of homolytic oxidation.

All homolytic electron transfer reactions, such as (7)–(9), require very much less activation energy than that needed for the direct breakage of a covalence. Hence homolytic oxidations, when once started, proceed very rapidly indeed. The traces of free radicals required for the initiation of homolytic oxidation may be formed by the thermal dissociation of molecules which have weak covalences, by disruption of molecules by exposure to radiant energy, high-energy particles (e.g. α-rays) or electrons (β-rays), or by single electron transfer from ions of transition elements which can have incomplete inner $(d, ..)$ electron shells. Consequently oxidations which are demonstrably prone to catalysis in these ways are homolytic in type.

Heterolytic oxidations involve the attack on organic compounds of electrophilic reagents which can, by a single process, gain control of a further electron pair. Heterolytic oxidants therefore attack the exposed electron pairs of atoms such as oxygen, nitrogen or sulphur, or the loosely held π-electrons of olefins, rather than the buried electron pairs of C—H, O—H or N—H bonds. Again, heterolytic reactions yield stable molecular, or ionic, products in one, or at most two consecutive stages and very seldom lead on to chain reactions. On the other hand they usually require more activation energy than homolytic reactions and so tend to be slower processes. They do not necessarily require catalysis, but even if this is so then the catalysts – bases, acids or Lewis acids – are quite different from those concerned in promoting homolytic reactions.

Stereochemical considerations are of much greater significance in heterolytic than in homolytic reactions, for in any heterolytic reaction, such as (6), the tetrahedral symmetry of the reaction product is related to that of the starting material, whilst in a homolytic reaction, such as (7), the free radical product has a planar distribution of the three remaining covalences about the carbon centre and so the following reaction, (8), yields a mixture of stereo-isomers.

A heterolytic oxidant approaches an organic molecule towards the region in which its valency electrons are most exposed: in extreme cases the products of electrophilic additions to bonds like C=C or C=O are stereospecific entities and not mixtures of isomers. Further, heterolytic oxidations often involve sequences of reactions ending with the elimination from an organic complex of the oxidant together with its extra electrons. A simple example is

10. $CH_3—CH_2—OH + Cl_2 \longrightarrow CH_3—CH_2—O—Cl + HCl$

11.
$$\begin{matrix} CH_3 \\ | \\ H—C—O—Cl \\ | \\ H \end{matrix} \longrightarrow \begin{matrix} CH_3 \\ | \\ H—C=O + H—Cl \end{matrix}$$

In the elimination process, (11), electron movements involve the C—H, C—O and O—Cl bonds *simultaneously*, for otherwise transient ions of very high energy content, e.g. $CH_3—CH_2—O^+$, would have to be formed. During the concerted reaction process the valency electrons of all the bonds concerned hybridize to yield the activated state with the minimum energy requirement, and since all bonds linking carbon atoms have some degree of spatial distinction (*p*-character) the optimum activated state is the one in which the affected bonds are all coplanar. With many eliminations a linear flow of electrons is promoted by the presence of an acid or base catalyst, but in several oxidations a cyclic electron flow occurs within an intermediate reaction complex.

These features of oxidation processes are illustrated in the following chapters.

CHAPTER 2

The Direct Oxidation of C—H Bonds

Autoxidation

The term autoxidation is applied generally to slow oxidations which can be effected by free oxygen (e.g. by air) at moderate temperatures and may be contrasted with the rapid processes of combustion or inflammation which require high temperatures. It has long been known that autoxidations are promoted by light and by small quantities of many catalysts, notably the oxides and oil-soluble salts of heavy metals, as well as by various peroxidic substances. Again they can be markedly retarded by mere traces of oxidizable organic substances, such as phenols and amines, many of which occur naturally as protectants of unrefined plant and animal products.

Analytical studies showed, many years ago, that, in the initial stages, *per*oxides are characteristic products of almost all the autoxidations of organic compounds, but that as the oxidation proceeds these peroxides break down to complex mixtures of more stable products. Paraffin hydrocarbons are much more resistant to autoxidation than are olefins, but the side chains of aromatic hydrocarbons are prone to attack. Amongst paraffinic hydrocarbons, substances containing tertiary C—H groups are most easily oxidized whilst CH_3 groups are the most resistant. Ethers are quite susceptible to autoxidation, whilst aldehydes are very much more easily attacked than are ketones. In all these compounds the initial oxidation product is a *hydroperoxide*. Thus ether gives (I), hexene-1 gives (II) and benzaldehyde (III).

$$CH_3-CH-O-C_2H_5 \qquad C_3H_7-CH-CH=CH_2 \qquad C_6H_5-C=O$$
$$\overset{|}{O}-OH \qquad\qquad \overset{|}{O}-OH \qquad\qquad \overset{|}{O}-OH$$
$$\text{I} \qquad\qquad\qquad \text{II} \qquad\qquad\qquad \text{III}$$

Several researches have shown that the autoxidation of olefinic compounds is, at room temperature, a homolytic chain reaction in which a trace of a free radical catalyst ($R\cdot$) produces, by dehydrogenation, an allylic radical. Reactions (2) and (3) thereupon continue as a chain sequence until the radicals (IV) or (V) are destroyed by some chain-breaking process.

1. $R \cdot + R_1—CH_2—CH=CH—R \longrightarrow R—H + R_1—\overset{\cdot}{C}H—CH=CH—R_2$

$$\updownarrow$$

$$R_1—CH=CH—\overset{\cdot}{C}H—R_2$$

$$IV$$

2. $R_1—\overset{\cdot}{C}H—CH=CH—R_2 + O_2 \longrightarrow R_1—CH(O—O \cdot)—CH=CH—R_2$

3. $R_1—CH—CH=CH—R_2 + R_1—CH_2—CH=CH—R$

$\underset{O—O \cdot}{|}$

$$V$$

$$\longrightarrow R_1CH—CH=CH—R_2 + R_1\overset{\cdot}{C}H—CH=CH—R_2$$

$$\underset{O—OH}{|}$$

The ease of autoxidation of olefins can be ascribed to the fact that the activation energy required to produce the mesomeric radical (IV) is much less than that required for the removal of a hydrogen atom from a —CH₂— group in a saturated paraffin chain and somewhat less than that required to add a radical R· to an ethylenic bond. As would be expected of the hybrid formula (IV), unsymmetrical olefins produce mixtures of isomeric hydroperoxides, whilst *cis*-olefins can isomerize to give *trans*-hydroperoxides. The great susceptibility of the 'drying oils', e.g. linoleates, towards autoxidation is due to the presence of the group —CH=CH—CH₂—CH=CH— in which *five* carbon atoms can be involved in a resonance system. Similarly, hydrocarbon chains attached to aromatic nuclei are invariably attacked in the α-position to give substituted benzyl radicals in which the odd electron can hybridize with the π-electrons of the benzene ring. Resonance stabilization of the initial radicals also affords explanations of the ease of autoxidation of aldehydes and ethers, whilst the reactivity of tertiary C—H groups in paraffins etc., is usually ascribed to hyper-conjugation (VI). With substituted benzaldehydes, polar substituents which favour the movement of electrons towards the CH=O group facilitate the homolytic abstraction of hydrogen. Thus an essential feature of the reaction

4. $\quad X—C_6H_4—CO—H + \cdot R \longrightarrow X—C_6H_4—CO \cdot + H—R$

is the tendency of the radical ·R to acquire control over a further electron.

Again aliphatic ketones can autoxidize by way of the resonance-stabilized radical

$$-\overset{|}{\underset{\cdot}{C}}—\underset{\underset{O}{\|}}{C}— \longleftrightarrow -\overset{|}{C}=\underset{\underset{O \cdot}{|}}{C}—$$

but the chains are much shorter than is the case for aldehyde autoxidation.

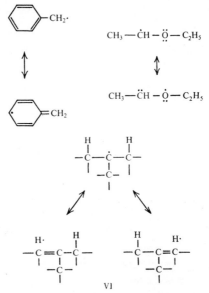

VI

Unlike ethers, alcohols are not easily autoxidized, for radicals $R_2\dot{C}$—OH are excellent chain-stopping agents,

5. $R_2\dot{C}$—OH + ·O—O—R' ⟶ R_2C=O + H—O—O—R'

and so a small percentage of an alcohol is regularly used to check the autoxidation of diethyl ether and also of chloroform. The latter is easily autoxidized, for in the ·CCl₃ radical the odd electron may be in part associated with any of the three chlorine atoms:

$$:\ddot{\underset{..}{C}l}—\dot{C}Cl_2 \longleftrightarrow :\dot{\underset{..}{C}l}—\ddot{C}Cl_2$$

The eventual reaction products are phosgene and hydrochloric acid, but the way in which the former is produced is not quite clear though the following reactions are possibilities:

6. $Cl_3C·$ + O_2 ⟶ Cl_3C—O—O·
7. Cl_3C—O—O· + H—CCl₃ ⟶ Cl_3C—O—O—H + ·CCl₃
8. Cl_3C—O—O·   ⟶ Cl_2C=O + ·O—Cl
9. Cl_3C—O—O—H   ⟶ Cl_3C—O· + ·OH
10. Cl_3C—O·   ⟶ Cl_2C=O + Cl·

In a corresponding manner pentachloroethane easily oxidizes to trichloroacetyl chloride,

$$Cl_3C-CHCl_2 \longrightarrow Cl_3C-CO-Cl$$

A number of commercially important olefins, such as styrene, butadiene and vinyl acetate, which do not contain allylic groups can nevertheless absorb oxygen slowly at room temperature. It is now known that these substances yield co-polymers with oxygen by reactions such as

11. $RO_2 \cdot + CH_2 = CHPh \longrightarrow RO_2 - CH_2 - \dot{C}HPh$

12. $RO_2 - CH_2 - \dot{C}HPh + O_2 \longrightarrow RO_2 - CH_2 - CHPh - O - O \cdot$

13. $RO_2 - CH_2 - CHPh - O - O \cdot + CH_2 = CHPh$
$\longrightarrow RO_2 - (CH_2 - CHPh - O - O) - CH_2 - \dot{C}HPh$

Of these (12) is fast, but (11) and (13) are much slower than reaction (14), the chain-propagating reaction of polymerization

14. $R' - CH_2 - \dot{C}HPh + CH_2 = CHPh$
$\longrightarrow R' - CH_2 - CHPh - CH_2 - \dot{C}HPh$

Consequently (12), which is an example of a *chain-transfer* reaction, checks the rate of polymerization of an olefin; it is so effective that many polymerizable olefins can be stored for days in open vessels without needing further protection by other additives, but the final 'drying' of an oil paint occurs largely through this initiation of polymerization (14) by surface autoxidation.

Catalysts of Autoxidation

Autoxidation commences by the production of a free radical that is capable of combining directly with free oxygen. Organic peroxides, such as benzoyl peroxide which dissociates thermally, or photochemically, as follows

15. $Ph.CO.O - O.CO.Ph \rightleftharpoons 2Ph.CO.O \cdot$
$Ph.CO.O \cdot \longrightarrow Ph \cdot + CO_2$

are effective catalysts for all autoxidations because they yield hydrocarbon radicals reactive enough to attack C—H bonds. Azo- and diazo-compounds are also effective catalysts. Some of these yield radicals that can attack C—H bonds but others, e.g. αα-azo-bis-isobutyronitrile (VII), give radicals that must first combine with oxygen before hydrogen abstraction can follow.

2

16. $Me_2C(CN)—N{=}N—CMe_2CN \longrightarrow N_2 + 2Me_2C(CN)\cdot$
                      VII

17. $Me_2C(CN)\cdot + O_2 \longrightarrow Me_2C(CN)—O—O\cdot$

Chlorine atoms are also highly effective autoxidation catalysts; bromine atoms are much less effective whilst iodine atoms inhibit autoxidation.

Small percentages of hydrogen bromide markedly promote the autoxidation of paraffin hydrocarbons by acting as a chain transfer agent; the following reactions are involved, e.g.

18. $R\cdot + H—Br$ $\longrightarrow R—H + Br\cdot$

19. $(CH_3)_3C—H + Br\cdot$ $\longrightarrow (CH_3)_3C\cdot + H—Br$

20. $(CH_3)_3C\cdot + O_2$ $\longrightarrow (CH_3)_3C—O—O\cdot$ } *both*

21. $(CH_3)_3C—O—O\cdot + H—Br$ $\longrightarrow (CH_3)_3C—O—O—H + Br\cdot$ } *fast*

22. $(CH_3)_3C—O—O\cdot + H—C(CH_3)_3 \longrightarrow (CH_3)_3C—O—O—H + \cdot C(CH_3)_3$

Reaction (22) is much slower than reaction (21), so that the bromine atoms maintain a higher concentration of the radicals $(CH_3)_3C\cdot$ than would otherwise be present.

Direct reactions of halogen atoms, such as reaction (19) above, are discussed on pp. 16 to 23.

Irradiation with ultra-violet light frequently initiates autoxidation and this is due to the absorption of enough energy to effect the homolysis of the organic compound and not the further activation of oxygen. Often the oxidation of purified conjugated dienes appears to set in without catalysis, but this is due to the fact that visible light can activate the system to a di-radical, capable of adding oxygen, by a non-chain reaction, so as to form a cyclic peroxide that easily undergoes thermal homolysis yielding a pair of chain-starting alkyloxy radicals:

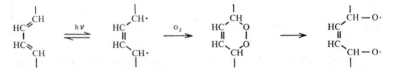

It is for this reason that 'boiled linseed oil' is used to hasten the drying of oil paints; the heating effects the isomerization

        $—CH{=}CH—CH_2—CH{=}CH— \longrightarrow —CH_2—CH{=}CH—CH{=}CH—$

These autoxidations can be promoted by 'photosensitizers', which are dyestuffs, such as eosin, or the natural colouring matter chlorophyll, which have strong absorption bands in the visible region and can easily transmit their absorbed energy to the unsaturated hydrocarbons. An important example of this is the synthesis of ascaridole from α-terpinene which can be promoted by the addition of a little methylene blue.

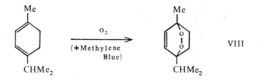

The pigments of boiled linseed-oil paints may act in a similar way.

The kinetics of autoxidation

(a) Catalysed reactions

The following schematic equations are relevant for the autoxidation of any compound R—H in the presence of an added catalyst (Cat.); they are also relevant for oxygen co-polymerization.

(i) $\quad$ Cat $\quad \xrightarrow{k_s}$ R· $\quad$ *chain starting*

(ii) $\quad$ R·$+O_2$ $\quad \xrightarrow{k_o}$ RO_2· $\quad$ ⎫

(iii) $\quad RO_2$·$+$R—H $\xrightarrow{k_p} RO_2$—H$+$R· ⎬ *chain sequence*

(iv) $\quad 2RO_2$· $\quad \xrightarrow{k_x}$ Products, X ⎫

(v) $\quad$ R·$+RO_2$· $\quad \xrightarrow{k_y}$ Products, Y ⎬ *chain ending*

(vi) $\quad$ 2R· $\quad \xrightarrow{k_z}$ Products, Z ⎭

The natures of the molecular products, X, Y and Z need not be specified.

If the reaction chains are long then, after a very brief period, the reaction will proceed at a steady rate, in which the total radical concentration remains constant, until either (a) an appreciable amount of the catalyst has been consumed or (b) the products, RO_2H, X, Y or Z are formed in sufficient amounts to affect chemically the reaction process.

In all known oxidations it has been found that k_o is 10^4 to 10^6 times k_p, and hence equation (iv) is the dominant chain-ending process. The steady-state condition may be written

(*Total rate of chain starting*) = (*Total rate of chain stopping*)

so that

$$k_s[\text{Cat}] = k_x[\text{RO}_2\cdot]^2$$

and hence

$$-d[\text{O}_2]/dt = k_o[\text{R}\cdot].[\text{O}_2] = k_p[\text{RO}_2\cdot].[\text{RH}] = k_p[\text{RH}]\left(\frac{k_s}{k_x}[\text{Cat}]\right)^{1/2}$$

It has, in fact, been found that the rates of autoxidation of almost all purified compounds are independent of the oxygen pressure, until values well below 100 mm total pressure have been reached.

The exact course of the chain-ending reaction (iv) varies from compound to compound and often it is still uncertain (see Chapter 3).

(b) Autocatalysed reactions

When autoxidizable substances have been purified until only minute traces (*ca.* 1 part per million) of radical-producing impurities are left then it is usually found that after prolonged storage in the presence of air they gradually become more and more prone to pick up oxygen, and that peroxidic impurities have accumulated in them. Careful trace analysis shows that the peroxide content of such autoxidizable substances progressively becomes less than that equivalent to the total volumes of oxygen which they have absorbed, and it has therefore been inferred that chain-starting radicals are being produced by the very slow homolysis of the initial peroxide, RO_2H. If added these peroxides indeed prove to be catalysts.

Now with ethyl linoleate, and some other purified olefins, it has been found that under conditions of autocatalysis the rate of autoxidation is proportional to the amount of oxygen that has been absorbed, i.e.

$$-d[\text{O}_2]/dt = k[\text{RO}_2\text{H}] \quad \text{(approx.)}$$

But for these substances the rate equation of the previous section is satisfied for catalysed reactions, so that for the *auto*catalysed reactions one can write

$$-d[\text{O}_2]/dt = k_p[\text{RH}].\left(\frac{k_s}{k_x}[\text{RO}_2\text{H}]^2\right)^{1/2}$$

which is rational only if the decomposition of the hydroperoxide is bimolecular, i.e.

(vii) $2\text{RO}_2\text{H} \longrightarrow$ Products containing free radicals

This seems to be a common feature of *hydro*peroxide decomposition and it appears that hydroperoxides easily form hydrogen-bonded dimers in quite dilute solution.

(c) Metallic ion catalysed reactions
Autoxidations are greatly accelerated, even in the dark, by the addition of *small* percentages of salts of manganese, iron, cobalt, copper and lead, particularly if oil-soluble salts, such as linoleates, stearates or naphthenates ('paint dryers') are used. In sunlight even colourless pigments, such as zinc and titanium oxides, can accelerate the autoxidation of paints, rubber and plastic articles, but such substances probably act by increasing the degree of absorption of radiant energy and so promoting hydroperoxide homolysis.

The ions of the transition metals, however, act by catalysing peroxide decomposition by routes (discussed in Chapter 3) which include both oxidations and reductions, e.g.

23. $\quad RO—OH + Fe^{2+} \longrightarrow RO\cdot + (Fe—OH)^{2+}$
24. $\quad RO—OH + Co^{3+} \longrightarrow RO—O\cdot + Co^{2+} + H^+$

and so generate oxy-radicals active enough to attack C—H bonds. If only small (under 1%) amounts of ions are used then the catalytic effect is proportional both to the concentration of the added ion and to the concentration of the peroxides initially present in the autoxidizing substance, but with concentrations of over 2% the efficacy of the additive falls off and ultimately the autoxidation rate, though high, is independent of the concentration of the added metallic ion. Eventually the rate of fresh hydroperoxide formation by autoxidation (the chain reaction, ii, iii) equals its rate of catalysed decomposition so that again oxygen uptake proceeds at a steady rate. Metallic ions have a negligible initial effect on the uptake of oxygen by hydrocarbons which have been freed very carefully from traces of peroxides, but manganic and cobaltic salts can directly oxidize both aldehydes and ketones to radicals capable of picking up oxygen (see Chapters 6 and 7).

Another feature of these metallic ion catalysed reactions is that a balance between the oxidation, (23), and reduction, (24), of the ions is reached, so that the catalyst retains its effectiveness. This balance depends on the redox potential of the metallic ion *in its particular environment*. Consequently, complexing agents, such as the anions of the organic acids used to produce the soluble salts, or added chelating agents, may greatly alter the catalytic efficiency of metallic ions. Some complexing agents, however, stabilize one valency level so effectively that they can check almost entirely a reaction such as (23) or (24): such substances are valuable additives for minimizing the autoxidation of lubricating oils which are continually liable to become contaminated by corrosion products from metallic machinery. However, the most effective metallic salt catalyst, or chelating protecting agent, for use in connection with any autoxidation depends both on the chemical nature of the organic compound which is being oxidized and on the operational temperature.

(d) Inhibited reactions

Very many substances contain small amounts of impurities which reduce their susceptibility to autoxidation, and often 'anti-oxidants' can be added in small percentages to check oxygen uptake still further. Probably no added 'inhibitor' checks autoxidation entirely, but it is easily possible to diminish by several thousand-fold the rate of autoxidation of a technical material, such as a hydrocarbon oil, without attempting by chemical means to free it from peroxides.

Provided that detectable oxidation does still occur (this can be ensured by the addition of a peroxide catalyst), it is possible to discover kinetically whether the velocity of any autoxidation is dependent upon the presence of an impurity and also something of the mode of action of the anti-oxidant.

If the anti-oxidant, A, acts by destroying $RO_2\cdot$ radicals then the chain-ending reaction (iv) of p. 11 must be replaced by (viii), whilst if it acts by destroying $R\cdot$ radicals then the dominant chain-ending is (ix)

(viii) $$RO_2\cdot + A \xrightarrow{k_A} \text{Inert product}$$

(ix) $$R\cdot + A' \xrightarrow{k'_A} \text{Inert product}$$

By making use of the steady-state condition it clearly follows that for chain-stopping via reaction (viii)

$$-d[O_2]/dt = k_p[RH]\left(\frac{k_s[\text{Cat}]}{k_A[A]}\right)$$

and for chain-stopping via (ix)

$$-d[O_2]/dt = k_o[O_2]\left(\frac{k_s[\text{Cat}]}{k_{A'}[A']}\right)$$

Both equations show first-order dependence upon [Cat]; thus square-root dependence upon [Cat] demonstrates the absence of inhibitor action – a valuable test for a trace impurity in an autoxidizable substance.

Again, the rate equations reveal the radical, $RO_2\cdot$ or $R\cdot$, that is concerned in the chain-ending process: thus inhibited reactions that are not oxygen pressure dependent have chains that are terminated by reactions between the inhibitor and peroxy radicals, $RO_2\cdot$. Nearly all anti-oxidants except quinones and some nitro-compounds have been shown to act in this way.

Sometimes, however, the reactions involving the additives (viii) or (ix) appear to be reversible. The substance A then acts as a *chain-transfer agent*; it merely diminishes but cannot suppress autoxidation.

Very much more is known about the inhibition of autoxidation from technological than from theoretical aspects, for today all commercial petroleum products, rubber articles, most synthetic plastics and even certain foodstuffs are regularly treated, before sale, with small amounts of anti-oxidants. The optimum inhibitor for economic use naturally depends upon the nature of the autoxidizable material which one wishes to stabilize and often questions of cost outweigh those of chemical efficiency. The most effective type of direct anti-oxidant now appears to be a highly alkylated phenol or aromatic amine. The amines have only a limited utility since they are soon oxidized to intensely coloured dyestuffs which detract from the value of the articles that they are intended to protect.

Many edible oils and fats, e.g. olive oil, cod-liver oil, butter and lard, contain appreciable percentages of olefinic esters and yet can be stored exposed to the air for long periods if kept from infection by moulds or bacteria. They do however contain traces of several potent natural anti-oxidants, such as quercitin (IX) and similar plant colours, tocopherol (X), vitamin-K and similar carotenoids, which, if destroyed by food-processing, e.g. fat-hardening, must be replaced by non-toxic additives. Propyl gallate (XI) has been used for this purpose.

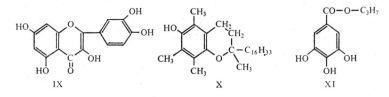

Recently it has been found that the efficacies of both phenol and amine anti-oxidants may be increased many times by admixture with organic sulphur compounds, such as thio-ethers, xanthates, dithiocarbamates and dithiophosphates. Some of these, which are fairly effective inhibitors on their own, may act by destroying peroxide molecules as well as radicals, whilst others, which have been found to be particularly valuable for the protection of lubricating oils, may act by destroying traces of catalytically active metallic ions. Typical of these sulphides is the lauroyl ester,

$$C_{11}H_{23}.CO.O—(CH_2)_3—S—(CH_2)_3—O.CO.C_{11}H_{23},$$

which is used, together with a phenol, for the stabilization of polypropylene.

It will be evident from the kinetic equation (viii) that if the inhibitor A is not itself a free radical then the initial attack on it by a $RO_2\cdot$ radical must give a new radical as the first reaction product. This new radical may react with itself, with a further $RO_2\cdot$ radical, or perhaps with radical $R\cdot$ or even with free oxygen. Each of these secondary reactions may again be chain-breaking processes with respect to the main autoxidation, and indeed the most effective technical inhibitors of autoxidation do terminate several reaction chains per molecule. Eventually, of course, the added inhibitor is completely destroyed or transformed into inert products. The circumstances become even more complex when it is desirable to find an inhibitor that can retain its effectiveness even in the presence of potentially catalytic metallic ions, such as those mentioned in the previous section. Some of the reactions involved in inhibitor action are dealt with in Chapter 9.

Homolytic halogenation

In Chapter 1 the chlorination of a paraffin was cited as a typical homolytic oxidation. Though in practice halogen substitution is often an inconvenient, indirect, oxidative route that has to be followed by a difficult heterolytic hydrolysis or elimination, its theoretical aspects are of great importance, for just as the study of autoxidation has revealed the way to control the kinetics of homolytic oxidations so the study of halogen substitution has given the most significant evidence concerning their structural features.

The direct chlorination of a liquid paraffin is a chain reaction requiring photochemical initiation:

25. $Cl—Cl \xrightarrow{hv} 2Cl\cdot$

26. $Cl\cdot + H—CR_3 \longrightarrow Cl—H + \cdot CR_3$ ⎫
                                                                                              ⎬ *a long chain*
27. $R_3C\cdot + Cl—Cl \longrightarrow R_3C—Cl + \cdot Cl$ ⎭

and is not very selective because reaction (26) is exothermic for all C—H bonds and requires little activation energy whilst reaction (27) is strongly exothermic. Hence an intractable mixture of products is often formed.

Chlorination by means of *sulphuryl chloride*, which is conducted in boiling carbon tetrachloride so that access of oxygen to the organic radicals is prevented, and requires catalysis by the thermal decomposition of an organic peroxide, or much better by αα-azo-bis-isobutyronitrile (VII, p. 10).

28. $Me_2C(CN)\cdot + SO_2Cl_2 \longrightarrow Me_2C(CN)—Cl + \cdot SO_2Cl$

29. $\cdot SO_2Cl \rightleftharpoons SO_2 + \cdot Cl$

30. $Cl\cdot + H—CR_3 \longrightarrow Cl—H + \cdot CR_3$

31. $R_3C\cdot + SO_2Cl_2 \longrightarrow R_3C—Cl + \cdot SO_2Cl$

seems to be slightly more selective and it has been shown that this change in selectivity for an apparently identical reaction, (26) and (30), is due to the choice of a different solvent (G. A. Russell, *J.A.C.S.* 1958, **80**, 4987 et seq.).

Another selective homolytic chlorinating agent is *tertiary butyl hypochlorite*, which has the great merit of not producing free hydrochloric acid. Its reactions are considered in Chapter 4.

It is much more difficult to understand why a solvent molecule should change the reactivity of a free atom or of a free radical than that of an ion, for all ions are known to be solvated in solution, and indeed the solvent effect upon radical reactions is smaller than that upon ionic reactions, but it is now clear that chlorine atoms are much less reactive in benzene or carbon disulphide than they are in paraffinic solvents. Whether this is due to the formation of solvated π-complexes, such as (XII), which could also be written for solvents such as carbon tetrachloride, or of covalently bonded σ-complexes (XIII), (XIV)

XII

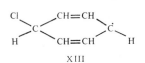

XIII

XIV

which like halogen atoms could dehydrogenate hydrocarbons, is as yet unknown.

Polar solvents, such as acetic acid, which would promote heterolytic reactions of chlorine, have to be avoided with these reagents. Similarly the halogenation of alcohols, ketones and even of carboxylic acids is usually a heterolytic reaction.

Much greater selectivity is found in homolytic *bromination*, for since the covalence H—Br is weaker than that of either H—Cl or H—C the reaction (32) is endothermic for any normal paraffin.

32. $$Br\cdot + H—CR_3 \longrightarrow Br—H + \cdot CR_3$$

However, bromination can directly be effected at the α-position to a benzene ring since, as with attack by $RO_2\cdot$ radicals (p. 71), the resulting benzylic radical has a resonance-stabilized structure and consequently the above reaction becomes exothermic. Thus one finds that cumene (XV) brominates only at the tertiary C—H group, but chlorinates also at the CH_3 groups; the latter attack is of course favoured statistically.

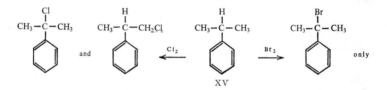

Even more selective in its action than bromine is *N-bromosuccinimide (NBS)*, (XVI), which was introduced in the 1940's as a specific agent for effecting the allylic substitution of unsaturated compounds, e.g.

$$NBS + CH_3—CH\!=\!CH—CO_2Me \longrightarrow Br—CH_2—CH\!=\!CH—CO_2Me$$

For this purpose it must be used in a non-ionizing solvent such as carbon tetrachloride, preferably with the addition of a small percentage of a radical-producing catalyst, such as αα-azo-bis-isobutyronitrile which has no undesired oxidizing action itself. Under these circumstances the real dehydrogenating agent is the succinimido radical (XVII).

In the absence of a catalyst the reaction depends on homolysis of the NBS which produces a minute concentration of bromine atoms. The special merit of N-bromosuccinimide depends on the facts (i) that

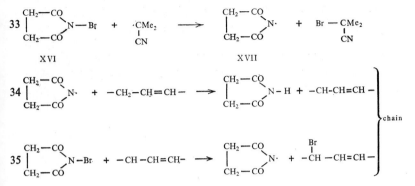

$$33 \quad \begin{matrix} CH_2-CO \\ | \qquad\qquad >N-Br \\ CH_2-CO \end{matrix} + \cdot CMe_2 \atop CN \longrightarrow \begin{matrix} CH_2-CO \\ | \qquad\qquad >N\cdot \\ CH_2-CO \end{matrix} + Br-CMe_2 \atop CN$$

XVI   XVII

$$34 \quad \begin{matrix} CH_2-CO \\ | \qquad\qquad >N\cdot \\ CH_2-CO \end{matrix} + -CH_2-CH=CH- \longrightarrow \begin{matrix} CH_2-CO \\ | \qquad\qquad >N-H \\ CH_2-CO \end{matrix} + -CH-CH=CH-$$

$$35 \quad \begin{matrix} CH_2-CO \\ | \qquad\qquad >N-Br \\ CH_2-CO \end{matrix} + -CH-CH=CH- \longrightarrow \begin{matrix} CH_2-CO \\ | \qquad\qquad >N\cdot \\ CH_2-CO \end{matrix} + \overset{Br}{-CH}-CH=CH-$$

} chain

the presence of molecular bromine is kept down to a minimum so that concurrent heterolytic addition of bromine to the double bond is avoided, and (ii) that the succinimido radical (XVII) itself, though a good dehydrogenating agent, has no tendency to add to a C═C bond. For similar reasons tertiary butyl hypochlorite is a specific allylic chlorinating agent. From the practical aspect, further advantages of N-bromosuccinimide are the absence of strongly acidic products, such as hydrogen bromide, and the insolubility of succinimide, which can often be removed quantitatively by filtration from the solution of the desired bromination product. N-bromosuccinimide should not be used in the presence of acids, for its cation (XVIII) is a heterolytic reagent which can effect bromination at C═C bonds or in aromatic nuclei.

$$36 \quad \begin{matrix} CH_2-CO \\ | \qquad >N< {}^{+H}_{Br} \\ CH_2-CO \end{matrix} + \begin{matrix} \diagdown C \diagup \\ \| \\ \diagup C \diagdown \end{matrix} \longrightarrow \begin{matrix} CH_2-CO \\ | \qquad\qquad >N-H \\ CH_2-CO \end{matrix} + \overset{+}{Br} \begin{matrix} \diagup C- \\ < \\ \diagdown C- \end{matrix}$$

XVIII

If used in very low concentration, in the presence of strong light, molecular bromine can effect allylic substitution (Sixma and Riem, *Proc. Acad. Sci. Amsterdam*, 1958, **B61**, 183) in preference to addition to a double bond and even molecular chlorine can be used for vapour phase allylic chlorination at high temperatures. This can be explained by the fact that the homolytic addition of halogen atoms to C═C bonds is a reversible process, whereas the addition of a bromine or chlorine atom to a hydrocarbon radical is irreversible (see p. 112).

The energetics of halogen abstractions, such as reactions (30) or (32), are not explicable only by reference to the energy content of the eventual radical •CR$_3$, for with both chlorinations and brominations it has been found that polar effects operate, though not so markedly as with heterolytic halogenations. Just as peroxy radicals attack substituted benzaldehydes less easily if electron-attracting substituents are present (reaction 4 of p. 7) so toluene derivatives containing nuclear halogen or nitro groups chlorinate or brominate less easily than does toluene itself.

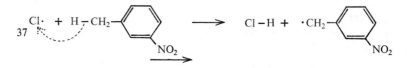

Reaction (37) involves electron withdrawal from the carbon atom of the CH$_3$ group and the polar effect of the electron-attracting nitro group hinders the reaction, even if the substituent is in the *meta* position so that its mesomeric effect is not involved.

In the case of chlorination, the polar effect of a substituent in the organic molecule concerned is more important than the degree of resonance stabilization of the resulting radical. Thus for butyric acid the relative percentage yields for chlorine atom attack are

$$CH_3—CH_2—CH_2—CO_2H \qquad\qquad CH_3—CH_2—\underset{\underset{Br}{|}}{CH}—CO_2H \quad XIX$$
$$31 \quad\ 64 \quad\ 5$$

whilst bromine gives only the α-bromo-acid (XIX). Clearly the resonance stabilization of the radical (XX)

$$C_2H_5—\overset{\bullet}{C}H—\underset{\underset{O—H}{|}}{C}=O \longleftrightarrow C_2H_5—CH=\underset{\underset{O—H}{|}}{C}—O\bullet \qquad XX$$

should, from enthalpy considerations, favour α-substitution, but the polar effect of the electron-attracting CO$_2$H group should make it more difficult to pull out a hydrogen atom from

$$H—\underset{|}{\overset{|}{C}}—CO_2H$$

than from

$$H—\underset{|}{\overset{|}{C}}—CH_2—CO_2H$$

since the electrical field due the dipole of the carboxyl group diminishes with the cube of the distance of separation.

It is now considered (G. S. Hammond, *J.A.C.S.* 1955, **77**, 334) that the polar effect is more important in chlorination than in bromination because with chlorination the energy maximum of the change (38):

38.   R₃C—H+·Cl ⟶ R₃C.....H.....Cl ⟶ R₃C·+H—Cl
           (transition state)

is reached when the C—H bond has only been stretched slightly whereas in bromination the point of energy maximum is reached when the separation of the ·CR₃ radical is almost complete. In this respect attack by succinimido radicals, and by peroxy radicals, R—O—O·, as in autoxidation, resembles bromination rather than chlorination, but attack by free hydroxyl radicals, ·OH, may resemble chlorination.

Steric hindrance to the removal of hydrogen from the surrounding groups, R, should be detectable though small, since hydrogen atoms are always exposed on the outside of organic molecules, but with branched paraffins the order of reactivity is tert. C—H > sec. CH₂ > CH₃, which is the sequence of bond strengths and can be ascribed qualitatively to 'hyperconjugation' (pp. 7–8) for if steric hindrance controlled reactivity the reverse order would be observed.

Stereochemical considerations however are important in the second stage of any homolytic halogenation, i.e.

27.   R₃C·+Cl—Cl ⟶ R₃C—Cl+·Cl

for though the weight of experimental evidence now indicates that the three covalences remaining in the R₃C· radical have a coplanar distribution, with the odd electron in a *p*-orbital at right angles to them, it does not follow that in a complicated molecule this *p*-electron should be equally accessible to attack from either side.

For instance, in the halogenation of norbornane, which first gives radical (XXI), attack with molecular chlorine, under irradiation, yields about 70% of the *exo*-chloride (XXII) and with sulphuryl chloride as much as 95% (Kooyman and Vegter, *Tetrahedron*, 1958, **4**, 322).

The stereochemistry of allylic substitution, however, has even greater theoretical significance. Walling and Thaler (*J.A.C.S.* 1961,

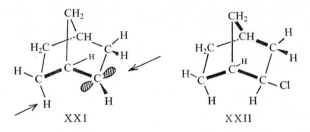

XXI   XXII

83, 3577) have shown that the chlorination of *trans*-2-butene (XXIII) by tert. butyl hypochlorite gave 80% of *trans*-1-chloro-2-butene (XXIV) and 20% of 3-chloro-1-butene (XXV), but no *cis*-1-chloro-2-butene (XXVI), whilst the chlorination of *cis*-2-butene (XXVII) gave 65% of *cis*-1-chloro-2-butene and no *trans*-isomer, though the chlorination of 1-butene (XXVIII) gave 70% of a mixture of the *cis*- and *trans*- isomers of 1-chloro-2-butene.

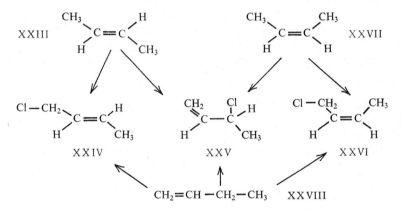

Similar results were obtained with the stereo-isomers of 4,4-dimethyl-2-pentene.

Thus it is clear that though hydrogen abstraction from both the butenes (XXIII) and (XXVII) yields a mesomeric allylic radical, usually shown schematically as

$$\cdot CH_2-CH=CH-CH_3 \longleftrightarrow CH_2=CH-\overset{\cdot}{C}H-CH_3$$

the radicals from (XXIII) and (XXVII) must have different, and not interchangeable, configurations with respect to the carbon centres of the original double bonds in the isomeric 2-butenes. One can see the

reason for this by drawing out the p- and π-orbitals of the radicals
(XXIX) and (XXX).

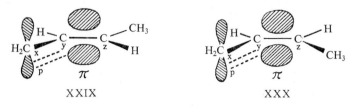

XXIX   XXX

The allylic system has a hybrid structure in which the single p-elec-
tron of the free radical and the two π-electrons of the adjacent olefinic-
link fuse together *because they are coplanar in orientation* and any
rotation about either the C_x—C_y or the C_y—C_z σ-bonds is thereby
prevented. Consequently if the chlorinating molecule (in this case
Me_3C—O—Cl) attacks the mesomeric radical at the more accessible
terminal carbon atom, C_x, then the product contains a C=C bond
between C_y and C_z *in its original configuration*, independently of the
side of approach of the chlorinating agent. However, if the reagent
approaches C_z then the new C=C bond is at C_x to C_y, whilst C_z,
though it becomes an asymmetric centre, can have the four substituent
groups arranged in either the d- or l-configurations.

This stereochemical consideration is significant also in connection
with the autoxidation of olefins, such as oleate and linoleate esters,
though this has not yet been explored experimentally. *Cis* ⇌ *trans*-
isomerization should occur *only* if there is a shift of a double bond.

Similar restrictions can hold for aromatic side-chain substitution,
for a benzylic radical (XXXI) will be resonance-stabilized only if the
p-electron can be oriented in the plane of the aromatic sextet and this
naturally locks the substituents A and B (fig. XXXII) into the plane of
the benzene ring.

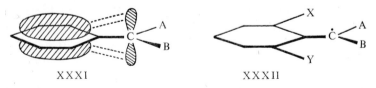

XXXI   XXXII

If large substituents, X, Y, obviate this possibility then the energetics
of the hydrogen abstraction:

$$C_6H_3XY-C(AB)-H + \cdot R \longrightarrow C_6H_3XY-C(AB)\cdot + H-R$$

become unfavourable. Kooyman and Strang have found that trichloro-
methyl radicals attack *meta-* or *para*-cymene about five times as
rapidly as they attack *ortho*-cymene (XXXIII).

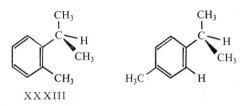

XXXIII

Photochemical reactions of quinones

When a quinone is irradiated it can be converted into an oxygen di-
radical, which, like any other radical R—O·, is capable of abstracting
hydrogen at room temperature from the C—H bonds of molecules of
several different types.

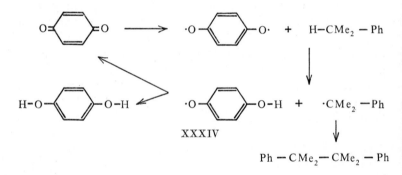

XXXIV

The resulting semiquinone radical (XXXIV), however, is a resonance-
stabilized aryloxy radical (see Chapter 9) and so is only a weak
oxidizer. It usually disproportionates to a mixture of a quinone and a
quinol (see Moore and Waters, *J. Chem. Soc.* 1953, 3405). Except in
hydrocarbon solutions, heterolytic reactions of quinones and quinols
may obscure this homolytic reaction unless the quinone ring itself is
fully substituted as in anthraquinone or phenanthraquinone. Radicals
such as $Ph.CMe_2$· in the example given above usually dimerize or
disproportionate, but radicals derived from alcohols, i.e. $R_2\overset{\cdot}{C}$—OH
may be strong enough reducing agents to react with unexcited quinone
molecules as follows,

$$R_2\dot{C}-OH \quad + \quad O=\!\!\langle \rangle\!\!=O \quad \longrightarrow \quad R_2C=O \quad + \quad H-O-\!\!\langle \rangle\!\!-O\cdot$$

so that, in total, light effects a non-chain oxidation:

$$\text{Alcohol} + \text{Quinone} \longrightarrow \text{Aldehyde} + \text{Quinol}$$

It has been suggested too that semiquinone radicals might be able to abstract hydrogen from organic molecules of certain types; in this event a chain reaction would set in. One example of this is the photochemical reaction between phenanthraquinone and benzaldehyde, where the chain process depends upon the addition of benzoyl radicals to quinone molecules.

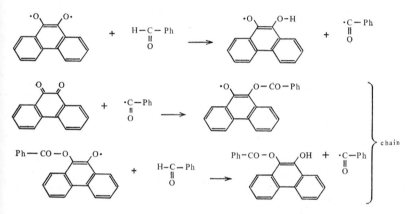

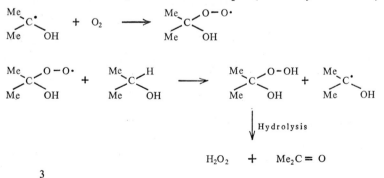

In the presence of oxygen the various types of radicals generated by this photochemical reaction may pick up oxygen and in this way an autoxidation chain may be set up. This reaction, which has been investigated in detail by Bolland and Cooper (*Proc. Roy. Soc.* 1954,

$$\underset{Me}{\overset{Me}{>}}\!\!C\!\!\overset{\cdot}{\underset{OH}{<}} \quad + \quad O_2 \quad \longrightarrow \quad \underset{Me}{\overset{Me}{>}}\!\!C\!\!\overset{O-O\cdot}{\underset{OH}{<}}$$

$$\underset{Me}{\overset{Me}{>}}\!\!C\!\!\overset{O-O\cdot}{\underset{OH}{<}} \quad + \quad \underset{Me}{\overset{Me}{>}}\!\!C\!\!\overset{H}{\underset{OH}{<}} \quad \longrightarrow \quad \underset{Me}{\overset{Me}{>}}\!\!C\!\!\overset{O-OH}{\underset{OH}{<}} \quad + \quad \underset{Me}{\overset{Me}{>}}\!\!C\!\!\overset{\cdot}{\underset{OH}{<}}$$

$$\downarrow \text{Hydrolysis}$$

$$H_2O_2 \quad + \quad Me_2C=O$$

3

A225, 405), explains why many vat dyestuffs tend to promote the rotting of fabrics – an effect that is particularly noticeable in window curtains. The addition of oxygen to semiquinone radicals, and to alcohol radicals can both lead to the formation of hydrogen peroxide: with isopropanol and with anthraquinone-β-sulphonic acid these reactions have been developed into commercial syntheses.

Similar photochemical reactions of benzophenone have been known for over 50 years. Thus on exposure to light a solution of benzophenone in isopropanol is converted to a mixture of benzpinacol and acetone.

$$Ph_2C{=}O \xrightarrow{\;h\nu\;} Ph_2\overset{\cdot}{C}{-}O\cdot$$

$$Ph_2\overset{\cdot}{C}{-}O\cdot + Me_2CH{-}OH \longrightarrow Ph_2\overset{\cdot}{C}{-}OH + Me_2\overset{\cdot}{C}{-}OH$$

$$Ph_2C{=}O + Me_2\overset{\cdot}{C}{-}OH \longrightarrow Ph_2\overset{\cdot}{C}{-}OH + Me_2C{=}O$$

$$2Ph_2\overset{\cdot}{C}{-}OH \longrightarrow Ph_2C(OH){-}CPh_2{-}OH$$

It may be noted that with benzophenone the hydrogen transfer takes place to the oxygen atom of the carbonyl group, for the radical $Ph_2\overset{\cdot}{C}{-}OH$ has much greater resonance stabilization than the alternative radical $Ph_2CH{-}O\cdot$ The radical $Ph_2\overset{\cdot}{C}{-}OH$, which has a comparable energy level to a semiquinone radical, is then too stable to attack isopropanol.

Several other photochemical oxidations of the above types have been described.

Other direct oxidations

Organic molecules of all types, including even the paraffins, can be oxidized, and partly are nitrated by *hot nitric acid*, which for this purpose need not be highly concentrated and is very effective in the vapour phase. Since this oxidation is promoted by the presence of oxygen and is retarded by nitric oxide it is thought to be a radical reaction initiated by the decomposition

$$HNO_3 \longrightarrow HO\cdot + NO_2$$

following which hydroxyl radicals would attack the hydrocarbon,

$$R{-}H + \cdot OH \longrightarrow R\cdot + H_2O$$
$$R\cdot + NO_2 \longrightarrow R{-}NO_2$$

Later stages of such oxidations may involve the formation and breakdown of alkyl nitrates or nitrites, which receive discussion in the following chapter. However, decisive evidence concerning the mechanism of nitric acid oxidation is meagre and all that can be said at present is that if hydrocarbon radicals are formed they must undergo very rapid subsequent reactions (see Duffin, Hughes and Ingold, *J. Chem. Soc.* 1959, 2734).

Chromic acid and *chromyl chloride* (Etard's reagent) also attack paraffin hydrocarbons and the general type of reactivity parallels that of chlorine atoms in regard to its degree of selectivity. The α-positions of aromatic side-chains, tertiary C—H groups of paraffins and cyclo-paraffins, and C—H groups adjacent to oxygen in ethers, are all susceptible to attack, but steric hindrance does not seem to be marked and differences in reactivity between different compounds of these various types are relatively small. Again C—D bonds are attacked more slowly than C—H bonds. Moreover these oxidations proceed more slowly in the complete absence of oxygen, which is absorbed to a slight extent by the reacting mixtures. Curiously enough the chromic acid oxidations, which are acid catalysed, occur at rates directly proportional to the total chromium-(VI) content of the oxidant solutions, which is not the case for heterolytic oxidations of alcohols, aldehydes or ketones (Chapters 4–7). Homolytic abstraction of hydrogen, possibly followed by an internal rearrangement of the initial reaction complex, has been tentatively suggested:

$$R_3C\text{---}H + Cr^{VI} \longrightarrow (R_3C\cdot \ .. \ H\text{---}Cr^V) \longrightarrow R_3C\cdot + Cr^V$$

$$\text{rapid} \downarrow \qquad\qquad \begin{array}{c}\textit{slight}\\ \textit{dissociation}\end{array}$$

$$R_3C\text{---}OH + Cr^{IV} \qquad R_3C\text{---}O\text{---}Cr^{IV}$$
$$\textit{hydrolysis}$$

(see Slack and Waters, *J. Chem. Soc.* 1948, 1666; 1949, 599: Wiberg *et al.*, *Tetrahedron*, 1960, **8**, 313; *J.A.C.S.* 1961, **83**, 423).

Undoubtedly the extent of *free* radical formation must be slight and the borderline between a homolytic oxidation and the heterolytic type of oxidation which can occur in allylic systems (Chapter 8) is indefinite.

With chromyl chloride, which is used in carbon disulphide or carbon tetrachloride solution, an insoluble adduct of the hydrocarbon with *two* molecules of the hydrocarbon is precipitated and there is no evolution of hydrogen chloride. It has been suggested that this adduct might be a double salt. Chromyl chloride is an effective oxidant for the methyl groups of toluene and its analogues with which the net reactions are

$$Ph.CH_3 \longrightarrow (Ph.CH_3,2CrO_2Cl_2) \longrightarrow Ph.CHO + 2Cr^{IV}$$

and the chromyl chloride, after hydrolysis of the adduct, is reduced to a mixture of 1 molecule of chromic acid to 2 molecules of a chromic salt. The aldehyde may be obtained in high yield by decomposing the addition complex with ferrous sulphate solution, when any further oxidation of the aldehyde by aqueous chromic acid is avoided.

Etard's reaction is a little-used oxidative procedure, possibly on account of the difficulty of handling chromyl chloride. A similar oxidation of $-CH_2-$ to $-CO-$ can be effected by using a cold solution of chromium trioxide in acetic anhydride, which is an excellent general solvent, but this method too has its experimental hazards, for chromium trioxide and acetic anhydride can react together violently if heated.

General reading references

BATEMAN, L., *Chem. Soc. Quart. Reviews*, 1954, **8**, 147 (Autoxidation).

BOLLAND, J. L., *Chem. Soc. Quart. Reviews*, 1949, **3**, 1 (Autoxidation).

INGOLD, K. U., *Chemical Reviews*, 1961, **61**, 563 (Inhibitors).

TEDDER, J. M., *Chem. Soc. Quart. Reviews*, 1960, **14**, 336 (Halogen reactions).

WALLING, C., *Free Radicals in Solution*, J. Wiley & Sons Inc., New York, 1957.

CHAPTER 3

Peroxides and their Reactions

In the preceding chapter it was pointed out that hydroperoxides R—O—O—H, were the initial reaction products of most autoxidations and that the catalysis of autoxidation could be ascribed to the homolytic breakdown of peroxidic substances. However, the chemistry of hydrogen peroxidic and its derivatives is very important *per se*; moreover it provides several mechanistic models for reactions of other oxidants that will receive mention later.

Preparation of peroxides
Hydrogen peroxide is an extremely weak acid ($K_1 = 1 \cdot 55 \times 10^{-12}$ at $20°$ C) but its hydroxyl groups generally behave like those of alcohols. Thus it is easily acylated or alkylated by acid-catalysed reactions, and by further reaction in neutral solution with acyl or alkyl halides one can form covalent diacyl or dialkyl peroxides, and also peroxy-esters which are soluble in organic solvents of all types.

1. $\quad$ H.CO.OH + HO—OH $\rightleftharpoons$ H.CO.O—OH + H$_2$O

2. $\quad$ Me$_3$C.OH + HO—OH $\underset{\text{H}^+}{\rightleftharpoons}$ Me$_3$C.O—OH + H$_2$O

3. $\quad$ 2Ph.CO.Cl + Na$_2$O$_2$ $\longrightarrow$ Ph.CO.O—O.CO.Ph + 2NaCl

4. $\quad$ Me$_3$C.O—O$^-$ + R—Br $\longrightarrow$ Me$_3$C.O—O.R + Br$^-$

Alkyl hydroperoxides also result from the autoxidation of hydrocarbons and from the addition of hydrogen peroxide to aldehydes and ketones, though the latter reaction may proceed further to yield cyclic polyalkylidene peroxides.

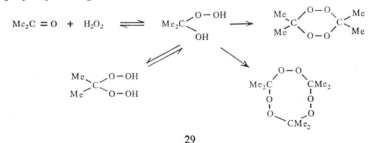

29

Solutions of many inorganic per-acids can be obtained by reactions of type (1), or by the use of acidic oxides and, in their reactions, resemble their organic analogues. A convenient way to obtain an-hydrous solutions of per-acids is by treatment of a diacyl peroxide with an equivalent of sodium ethoxide:

5. $Ph.CO.O—O.CO.Ph + EtONa \longrightarrow Ph.CO.O.Et + Ph.CO.O—ONa$

After separation of the ester the free per-acid can be liberated with an equivalent of a stronger acid and extracted into a solvent such as chloroform. Several aromatic per-acids can however be obtained as crystalline solids.

Though all peroxidic compounds are potentially explosive many useful reagents need only be prepared *in situ* in cold dilute solution. In general, covalent peroxides in non-ionizing solvents undergo homo-lytic reactions, whilst the polar per-acids have heterolytic reactivity especially in polar solvents.

Homolytic decomposition reactions

Benzoyl peroxide, $Ph.CO.O—O.CO.Ph$, and its aromatic analogues, are relatively safe substances which can be purified by crystallization, or better by precipitation from organic solvents. When heated in non-ionizing solvents these peroxides decompose in stages (6, 7) but in concentrated solutions a chain reaction (8, then 7) may set in.

6. $Ph.CO.O—O.CO.Ph \rightleftharpoons 2Ph.CO.O\cdot$

7. $Ph.CO.O\cdot \longrightarrow Ph\cdot + CO_2$

8. $Ph\cdot + Ph.CO.O—O.CO.Ph \longrightarrow Ph.CO.O.Ph + Ph.CO.O\cdot$

With benzoyl peroxide itself these reactions occur at a reasonable rate in the temperature range 70–100°.

The use of benzoyl peroxide as an autoxidation catalyst has already been mentioned; diacyl peroxides are even more frequently used as catalysts for initiating the homolytic addition and polymerization reactions of olefins and a wide range of compounds is now available so that an appropriate catalyst may be chosen for use at any desired temperature between 0° and 150°. *Acetyl peroxide*, $(Me.CO.O—)_2$, must be handled with great care since it is slightly volatile and liable to explode, but *lauroyl peroxide* $(C_{11}H_{23}.CO.O—)_2$, is a much safer reagent.

Since, in dilute solution, acetyl peroxide decomposes quantitatively according to the equation

9. $\quad\quad$ Me.CO.O—O.CO.Me $\longrightarrow$ 2Me· + 2CO$_2$

it has been used extensively in quantitative studies of the reactions of methyl radicals, which dehydrogenate paraffins, alcohols or ethers but add on to both olefinic and aromatic compounds. On the preparative scale, however, a much safer source of methyl radicals is *di-tert. butyl peroxide*, a liquid which decomposes smoothly in the 110–150° range as follows, without any appreciable chain decomposition.

10. $\quad\quad$ Me$_3$C.O—O.CMe$_3$ $\longrightarrow$ 2Me$_3$C—O·

11. $\quad\quad$ Me$_3$C—O· $\quad\quad\longrightarrow$ Me$_2$C=O + Me·

The different types of radicals exemplified by Phenyl, Ph·, Methyl, Me·, tert. Butoxy, Me$_3$C—O· and Benzoyloxy, Ph.CO.O·, are all dehydrogenating agents, but with greatly differing degrees of reactivity, which decrease in the order given above.

Other useful sources of alkyloxy radicals, R—O·, are the percarbonates,

12. $\quad\quad$ R.O.CO.O—O.CO.O.R $\longrightarrow$ 2R—O· + 2CO$_2$

and the percarbonic and peroxalic esters,

13. $\quad\quad$ R.O—O.CO.O.R $\quad\quad\longrightarrow$ 2R—O· + CO$_2$

14. $\quad\quad$ R.O—O.CO.CO.O—O.R $\longrightarrow$ 2R—O· + 2CO$_2$

which are controllable catalysts for use at low temperatures since the liberation from them of large volumes of carbon dioxide provides a built-in safety factor. Many other peroxy-esters have been developed as technical catalysts.

The decomposition (11) of an alkyloxy radical may yield a mixture if different groups are present, e.g.

15. $\quad$ Me$_2$CEt—O· $\longrightarrow$ Me$_2$C=O + ·Et $\quad$ or $\quad$ Me—CO—Et + ·Me

but naturally the two products of least total energy will preponderate. Thus a primary or secondary alkyloxy radical will always yield an aldehyde and an alkyl radical rather than atomic hydrogen (though this may be formed from CH$_3$—O· or HO—CH$_2$—O·) whilst a radical containing an α-aryl substituent, e.g. Ph.CMe$_2$—O·, will always yield an aromatic ketone or aldehyde rather than a free aryl radical. The ease of elimination of alkyl radicals is, in general, tertiary > secondary > primary > methyl.

The decomposition of a dialkyl peroxide containing only aryl groups is followed by the migration of an aryl group from carbon to oxygen and the secondary radical thus formed is not an oxidizing agent and merely dimerizes.

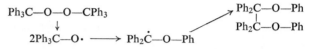

$$Ph_3C—O—O—CPh_3$$
$$\downarrow$$
$$2Ph_3C—O \cdot \longrightarrow Ph_2\overset{\cdot}{C}—O—Ph$$

$$Ph_2C—O—Ph$$
$$Ph_2C—O—Ph$$

However there is no evidence that alkyl groups can migrate in a similar fashion.

Higher alkyl radicals may decompose thermally giving smaller radicals and olefins:

16. $$CH_3—CH_2—CH_2 \cdot \longrightarrow CH_3 \cdot + CH_2{=}CH_2$$

This occurs easily at the high temperatures of gas phase oxidations and is the process that occurs in the thermal depolymerization of macro-molecules.

Polymeric peroxides, such as the co-polymers of olefins with oxygen, yield relatively few radicals when they decompose, for macro-radicals rapidly depolymerize by reactions similar to (11) and (16) above, giving simple aldehydes or ketones. For instance the autoxidation of styrene gives mainly benzaldehyde and formaldehyde, for the initial co-polymer decomposes significantly even at the temperature appropriate for autoxidation. The following diagram shows why these reaction products are to be expected, for each homolysis is exothermic because it gives a simple molecule with a C=O bond.

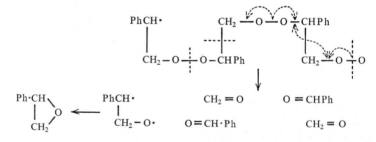

Styrene oxide however is a minor reaction product. It could be formed as the end-product of the depolymerization of a slowly-growing polymer radical.

Much of the information summarized above concerning the decomposition reactions of dialkyl peroxides has been gained from gas phase studies. Whilst it is of much value in interpreting the course of gas phase combustions of organic compounds it is also helpful in the elucidation of the mechanisms of the homolytic oxidations of alcohols which are considered in Chapter 4. However, for the interpretation of liquid phase reactions of organic compounds these unimolecular decomposition processes should be invoked with some reserve, except for reactions carried out under conditions of high dilution in an inert solvent. Chain reactions, such as the decomposition (equation 8, p. 30) of benzoyl peroxide which yields phenyl benzoate, diminish greatly the yield of free radicals per peroxide molecule decomposed. Again, in more concentrated solutions, reactions between radicals can give molecular products other than dimers. Thus butylene oxide is one product of the decomposition of ditertiary butyl peroxide.

17. $\qquad CH_3\cdot + (CH_3)_3C—O\cdot \longrightarrow CH_4 + CH_2\overset{\displaystyle\frown}{\underset{O}{}}C(CH_3)_2$

These bimolecular reactions are not of great importance when peroxides are used in small amounts, as in the catalysis of olefin polymerization or of autoxidation, but they can complicate seriously the ultimate composition of the reaction product when a peroxide is used as a prime oxidizing agent.

So if it is desired to oxidize organic compounds by alkyl, alkyloxy or acyloxy radicals it is strongly advisable to use the simplest possible compound that is known to decompose, without danger, in the required temperature range, i.e. benzoyl peroxide between 70 and 100° and tertiary butyl peroxide between 110 and 150°.

In contrast to the dialkyl and diacyl peroxides, the alkyl and acyl *hydroperoxides* are both of very limited value as direct sources of oxidizing radicals since, even in dilute solution, they tend, like carboxylic acids or alcohols, to associate together and predominantly decompose to molecular rather than radical products. Thus, even in dilute solution in chlorobenzene, tertiary butyl hydroperoxide decomposes almost quantitatively to tertiary butanol and oxygen. Some radicals are formed since the decomposition does catalyse olefin polymerization, so that a chain reaction could be formulated, e.g.

18. $Me_3C—O—OH \qquad\qquad \longrightarrow Me_3C—O\cdot + \cdot OH$

19. $Me_3C—O\cdot + H—O—O—CMe_3 \longrightarrow Me_3C—OH + \cdot O—O—CMe_3$

20. $2Me_3C—O—O\cdot \qquad\qquad \longrightarrow 2Me_3C—O\cdot + O_2$

or, alternatively a cyclic decomposition could be proposed.

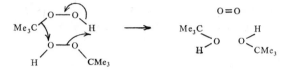

The latter is certainly true for the base-catalysed decomposition of any hydroperoxide (see p. 46).

Decompositions of both primary and secondary hydroperoxides may include some chain-branching reactions and can be of explosive violence. From primary alkyl hydroperoxides even molecular hydrogen may be one reaction product.

Per-acid decompositions yield mainly oxygen together with the corresponding carboxylic acid, but smaller amounts of carbon dioxide and of the lower alcohol are also formed.

The decomposition of peroxy radicals, $R—O—O\cdot$, which may be invoked in formulating reactions schemes such as the chain reaction given above, is important in connection with the chain-ending process of autoxidation. It is usually written as

20′. $2R—O—O\cdot \longrightarrow 2R—O\cdot + O_2 \longrightarrow R—O—O—R$

and there is clear evidence that it does include oxygen evolution, but the actual reaction process seems to differ from radical to radical. If the radical contains an α-hydrogen atom then a mixture of an alcohol and a ketone is formed by a cyclic process, such as

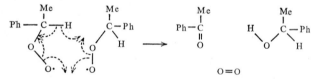

but tertiary radicals appear to give some olefinic product.

21. $2Ph—CMe_2—O—O\cdot \longrightarrow Ph—CMe_2—O—OH + Ph—\underset{\underset{Me}{|}}{C}{=}CH_2 + O_2$

Uses of radicals as oxidizing agents

Many reactions of the types

22. $R\cdot + H—R' \longrightarrow R—H + \cdot R'$: $RO\cdot + H—R' \longrightarrow ROH + \cdot R'$

have been mentioned in the previous pages. They can all be applied for the specific dehydrogenation of organic molecules when the reactivity of the secondary radical, $\cdot R'$, can be predicted. Thus peroxide decompositions can conveniently be used to prepare compounds of the bibenzyl series:

23. $RO\cdot + C_6H_5.CH_3 \longrightarrow C_6H_5-CH_2\cdot$

$$\longrightarrow C_6H_5-CH_2-CH_2-C_6H_5$$

and also to prepare 1,4-diketones

24.
$$RO\cdot + \begin{matrix} -CH_2 \\ | \\ -CO \end{matrix} \longrightarrow \begin{matrix} -CH\cdot \\ | \\ -CO \end{matrix} \longrightarrow \begin{matrix} -CH-CH- \\ | \quad | \\ -CO \quad CO- \end{matrix}$$

but this reaction is accompanied by disproportionation to olefins, e.g.

25.
$$\underset{\overset{|}{CH_3}}{Ph-\overset{\cdot}{C}-CH_3} + \cdot OR \longrightarrow \underset{\overset{|}{CH_3}}{Ph-C{=}CH_2} + HOR$$

and so the reaction can be used, though not very effectively, for the aromatization of cycloparaffin rings.

In aliphatic chemistry one of the first applications of this reaction was for the oxidation of acetic acid to succinic acid by the action of acetyl peroxide. When this oxidation is applied to homologues or derivatives of acetic acid then radicals with three different substituent groups result, and consequently the dimeric product contains two asymmetric centres. Though optically inactive it is *not* an equimolar mixture of *racemic* and *meso* forms; the latter preponderates for it has the more stable configuration. Thus the action of acetyl peroxide on chloroacetic acid gives *meso*-αβ-dichlorosuccinic acid in which the big groups are most widely separated.

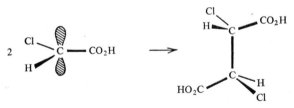

It is worth noting that the corresponding reaction with bromo-acetic acid yields succinic acid, because the bond strength of C—Br is so much less than that of either C—Cl or C—H.

26. $\cdot CH_3 + Cl-CH_2-CO_2H \longrightarrow CH_4 + \cdot CHCl-CO_2H$

but

27. $\cdot CH_3 + Br-CH_2-CO_2H \longrightarrow CH_3-Br + \cdot CH_2-CO_2H$

A useful application of radical oxidation is for the fission of ethers, which are attacked at C—H groups adjacent to oxygen, e.g.

28. $Ph.CH_2—O—CH_2.Ph \longrightarrow Ph—\overset{\cdot}{C}H—O—CH_2—Ph$
$$\longrightarrow Ph—CHO + \cdot CH_2—Ph$$

The C—O bond fission occurs only if a fairly stable hydrocarbon radical can be formed: otherwise the ether radical dimerizes. It is important to note this reaction, for it means that though ethers are excellent choices as inert solvents in which to effect heterolytic reactions they should not be selected for homolytic reactions.

Many of these oxidations by alkyloxy radicals can also be effected by the catalysed homolytic decompositions of peroxides which are discussed in the following section.

Similar reactions also result from the decomposition of aqueous solutions of organic compounds by ionizing radiations (α, β, γ or X-rays) for the primary act of radiolysis gives hydrogen atoms and hydroxyl radicals, both of which can exothermically dehydrogenate C—H bonds.

29. $H_2O \quad \rightsquigarrow (H_2O)^+ + e$

30. $(H_2O)^+ \longrightarrow H^+ + \cdot OH$

31. $e + H_2O \longrightarrow (H_2O)^- \longrightarrow H\cdot + (OH)^-$

Again if oxygen is present, as is the case in all solutions exposed to the air, hydroperoxy radicals, H—O—O$\cdot$ are immediately formed from the hydrogen atoms. The subsequent reactions of these radicals, H—O$\cdot$, or H—O—O$\cdot$, formed by these high-energy routes, are however identical with the reactions described elsewhere in this chapter. The unique feature of radiochemical reactions is the location of the initial disruption of a molecule into an active particle: it may occur in the middle of a bulk of a solution, or of a solid substance such as an organic polymer, and even within a cell of living tissue.

The latter eventuality is applied beneficially in medical radiotherapy, but is the crucial hazard of 'radiation damage' that might eventuate from atomic warfare.

Catalysed homolytic decompositions of peroxides

In 1894 H. J. H. Fenton discovered that the addition of a ferrous salt initiated the rapid oxidation by hydrogen peroxide of α-hydroxy-acids, such as tartaric acid, and of α-glycols, but his reagent did not receive wide application until, about 50 years later, it was discovered in technical laboratories in both England and Germany that the peroxide-catalysed polymerization of olefins in aqueous emulsions could be markedly promoted by the addition of a reducing agent, such as Fe^{2+}, which could only give up one electron to an acceptor molecule. It was then shown, by M. G. Evans and his colleagues, that the polymerization was effected by hydroxyl radicals produced as follows:

32. $Fe^{2+} + HO-OH \longrightarrow (Fe-OH)^{2+} + \cdot OH$

33. $HO\cdot + CH_2{=}CHR \longrightarrow HO-CH_2-CHR\cdot$

$$\longrightarrow HO-(CH_2-CHR)_n\cdot$$

By that time it was known that hydroxyl radicals, which could be produced, with difficulty, by irradiating hydrogen peroxide with ultra-violet light, were exceedingly powerful oxidizing agents and a broad survey of the oxidizing properties of hydrogen peroxide in the presence of ferrous sulphate showed that organic compounds of nearly all types could be oxidized by this 'Fenton's reagent', though naturally it could only be used effectively for attacking water-soluble substances in acid solution (Merz and Waters, *J. Chem. Soc.* 1949).

The oxidations can be classified into two groups – (i) chain reactions, in which only a small amount of reducing agent is needed, and (ii) non-chain reactions in which all the oxidation is effected by hydroxyl radicals formed by reaction (31) and there is considerable loss due to the following reaction (34)

34. $$Fe^{2+} + \cdot OH \longrightarrow (Fe-OH)^{2+}$$

Primary and secondary alcohols, aldehydes and ethers oxidize by the chain reaction, which has now been proved to depend on the fact that these substances yield organic radicals that are capable of reducing ferric ions, and others of similar redox potential (e.g. Hg^{2+}).

35. $$HO\cdot + CH_3-CH_2.OH \longrightarrow H_2O + CH_3.\overset{\cdot}{C}H-OH$$

36. $$CH_3.\overset{\cdot}{C}H-OH + Fe^{3+} \longrightarrow CH_3.CH{=}O + H^+ + Fe^{2+}$$

The chain reaction which depends upon the reduction (36) of the ferric ion can be eliminated by adding a fluoride, which at once converts the ferric ion to a stable complex, $(FeF_6)^{3-}$, or by ethylene-diamine tetra-acetic acid (EDTA) which acts in a similar manner, and can be diverted by adding a more reducible substance, such as a mercuric salt:

37. $$CH_3-\overset{\cdot}{C}H-OH + Hg^{2+} \longrightarrow CH_3-CH{=}O + Hg^+ + H^+$$

or, of course, by adding a polymerizable olefin. The promotion of a reduction (reaction 37) by an oxidative process can be used as a diagnostic test for a homolytic reaction.

So effective can be this reducing action of such radicals that in technical mixtures for effecting emulsion polymerization it is now customary to add a substance, such as glucose, to maintain the activity of the metallic ion promoter. Reaction (36) being followed by (32) of course keeps up a constant supply of hydroxyl radicals until the peroxide is exhausted.

It has been found that the oxidation of a hydrocarbon radical by an ion such as Fe^{3+} or Cu^{2+} is also a chain-ending process in emulsion polymerization

38. $-CH_2-CH(R)\cdot + Fe^{3+} \longrightarrow -CH=CHR + Fe^{2+} + H^+$

and so, even with polymerizations that have been started with free radical catalysts, such as αα-azo-bis-isobutyronitrile, or by the action of ionizing radiations, it is possible to control the average molecular weight of the polymer by adding an appropriate concentration of reducible metallic ions.

Aromatic compounds can be either dimerized or hydroxylated by Fenton's reagent and a careful study with benzene has shown that the conversion of the hydrocarbon to the phenol depends upon the presence of a high concentration of ferric ions, for otherwise the oxidation of the primary adduct is much slower than its dimerization.

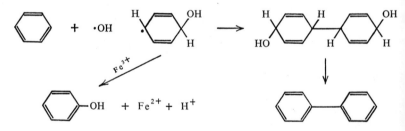

Since even the hydrocarbon chains of aliphatic acids are attacked to some extent by hydroxyl radicals, Fenton's reagent can only be used effectively as an oxidant when one can make use of a chain reaction, such as that of alcohol oxidation (above). With substances (e.g. many phenols) which can be oxidized directly by ferric ions the overall reaction may be very complex indeed.

The physical chemistry of reactions between salts of iron and hydrogen peroxide has been investigated in great detail, for this system is a model for the understanding of the actions of the important enzymes *catalase* and *peroxidase*. In the presence of mineral acid the overall reaction

$$2Fe^{2+} + H_2O \rightleftharpoons 2Fe^{3+} + 2(OH)^-$$

is quantitative, but as the pH is raised there is some evolution of oxygen due to the reactions:

39. $HO—OH \rightleftharpoons HO—O^- + H^+$

40. $Fe^{3+} + HO—O^- \longrightarrow Fe^{2+} + HO—O\cdot$

41. $HO—O\cdot \rightleftharpoons H^+ + (O—O\cdot)^-$

42. $Fe^{3+} + (O—O\cdot)^- \longrightarrow Fe^{2+} + O_2$

and in alkaline solution a ferric complex, e.g. $\{Fe(CN)_6\}^{3-}$, may be reduced quantitatively by hydrogen peroxide. Even in acid solution, cobaltic, manganic and ceric ions are reduced in this way.

Reactions (40) to (42) involve not hydroxyl but *hydroperoxy radicals* (H—O—O• or its anion); these too can attack many organic molecules, but in a different manner to, and much less effectively than, hydroxyl radicals. For example, hydroperoxy radicals do not oxidize aliphatic alcohols. Norman and Radda (*Proc. Chem. Soc.* 1962, 138) have shown that it is possible to discriminate between these two types of radicals by measuring the percentage yields of *ortho-*, *meta-* and *para-*hydroxylation products that they produce with simple benzene derivatives. They have shown that the oxidizing reagent obtained by blowing oxygen through a solution containing ascorbic acid and ferrous ions, which has been used as a model system to simulate metabolic hydroxylations, yields hydroperoxy radicals and not hydroxyl radicals. Which radical, H—O• or H—O—O•, is predominantly concerned in several catalysed reactions that can be effected in nearly neutral solutions of hydrogen peroxide is still uncertain. Thus Ruff's important degradation of sugar lactones (p. 40) by hydrogen peroxide and ferric acetate in a buffered solution may largely involve $HO_2\cdot$, for the •OH radical would undoubtedly attack each alcoholic group of the carbohydrate derivatives. There is a similar uncertainty concerning the mechanism of action of peroxidase enzymes.

Organic hydroperoxides and per-acids can replace hydrogen peroxide in nearly all of the catalysed reactions that have been mentioned

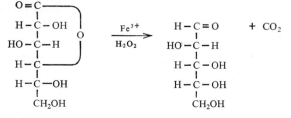

above. It has been shown by M. S. Kharasch and his colleagues that the one-electron reduction of an organic hydroperoxide always yields an alkyloxy radical rather than hydroxyl, thus:

43. $Me_3C—O—OH + Fe^{2+} \longrightarrow Me_3C—O\cdot + (Fe—OH)^{2+}$

and this route is the most convenient way for generating with safety the various types of alkyloxy radicals mentioned in the previous section. Again, reactions such as

44. $Me_3C—O—OH + Co^{3+} \longrightarrow Me_3C—O—O\cdot + Co^{2+} + H^+$
45. $Me_3C—O—O\cdot + Co^{3+} \longrightarrow Me_3C^+ + Co^{2+} + O_2$

which reduce the ions of transition metals, together with reactions such as (43) which oxidize them, account for the catalytic effects of such ions on autoxidations (Chapter 2).

As direct oxidants, alkyloxy radicals are much less powerful than free hydroxyl (hence the course of reaction 43) but they can, like them, add on to olefinic bonds, and the thermal breakdown of alkyloxy radicals produced by reduction of hydroperoxides can have valuable applications, one of which is shown below.

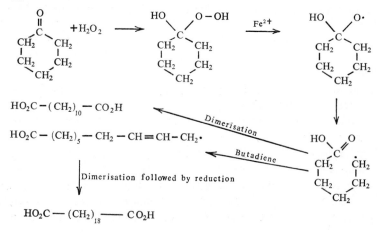

Similar reactions can occur with peroxy-esters and with dialkyl peroxides, including the trans-annular peroxides that may be obtained by photochemical addition of oxygen to conjugated dienes. An interesting example of this is afforded by the reduction of ascaridole (I) by either titanous or ferrous salts (Davis, Halsall and Hands, *Proc. Chem. Soc.* 1961, 83). The isopropyl radical is eliminated and in part recombines with the double bond of the resulting αβ-unsaturated ketone. With dihydro-ascaridole (II) the propyl radical is eliminated as propane, following titanous chloride reduction, though the pyrolysis of dihydro-ascaridole yields ethylene.

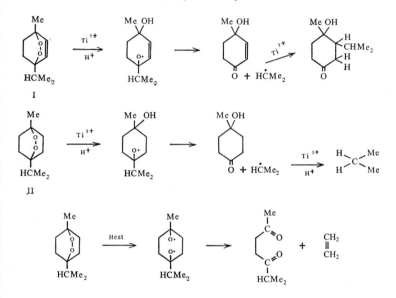

Heterolytic decompositions of peroxides

Organic and inorganic per-acids, and to a less extent the organic hydroperoxides, are polarized molecules and consequently there is an inherent tendency for their weak O—O bonds to break heterolytically:

$$\underset{O}{\overset{R}{}}C-O{-}OH \longrightarrow \underset{O}{\overset{R}{}}C-O^- + (OH)^+$$

However, *free* oxy-cations, HO^+, RO^+, would be particles of such high energy content that they are never formed: *all heterolytic reactions of*

4

peroxy-compounds are bimolecular, i.e. (46) *unless stereochemically similar intramolecular rearrangements are involved.*

46. $R—O—O—H + :X \longrightarrow (R—O:)^- + H—O—X$

The simple bimolecular reaction indicated above can be exemplified by the peroxide oxidation of many molecules which contain available unshared electron pairs, e.g.

Tertiary amines including:
(*a*) Pyridine bases:

$$R_3N: + HO—OR \longrightarrow R_3\overset{+}{N}—OH \longrightarrow R_3N{\rightarrow}O \quad \text{Amine oxides}$$

(*b*) Sulphides:

$$R_2\overset{..}{S}: \longrightarrow R_2\overset{..}{S}{\rightarrow}O \quad \text{Sulphoxides}$$

(*c*) Phosphines, Phosphites:

$$R_3P: \longrightarrow R_3P{\rightarrow}O \quad \text{Phosphates}$$

(*d*) Azo compounds:

$$Ar—N{=}N—Ar \longrightarrow \underset{\underset{O}{\downarrow}}{Ar—N{=}N—Ar} \quad \text{Azoxy compounds}$$

(*e*) Aryl iodides:

$$Ar—I \longrightarrow Ar—I{\rightarrow}O \quad \text{Iodoso compounds}$$

Naturally these reactions are facilitated by the stability of the leaving group, $(OR)^-$, and hence the reactivity of a per-acid HO—O—Acyl depends on the strength of the parent acid H—O—Acyl. Thus performic acid is more reactive than peracetic acid and per-trifluoroacetic acid is an electrophilic agent that is powerful enough to hydroxylate even aromatic nuclei. Hydrogen peroxide itself will react in a similar manner in the presence of an acid catalyst,

47. $$HO—OH + H^+ \rightleftharpoons H—O—\overset{+}{O}\!\!\begin{smallmatrix} H \\ H \end{smallmatrix}$$

so that most of the reactions listed above can be carried out with solutions of hydrogen peroxide in an organic acid.

The *Prilesajew reaction* between a per-acid and an olefin is a similar bimolecular reaction in which the π-electrons of an olefin are attacked,

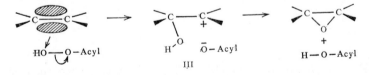

but it is most easily carried out in a non-ionizing solvent such as benzene or chloroform, so that the intermediate complex is probably covalently bonded (IV) and not a dissociating ion-pair (III).

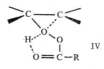

As the diagram above indicates, the π-electrons of an olefin extend most in the plane perpendicular to that containing the four atoms attached to the C=C bond, and consequently the per-acid attacks at right angles to the plane of these atoms. Consequently when a cyclic olefin is attacked the oxygen atom of the resulting epoxide takes up an *axial* position (V), and with a rigid molecule, such as cholesterol, the π-bond is attacked from the less hindered (α) side, (VI).

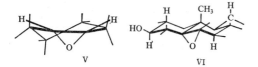

Epoxides can be hydrolysed by both acids or bases, though in practice their acid hydrolysis is the more convenient experimentally. In both cases the ring fission is a bimolecular process (S_N2) in which the entering hydroxyl approaches the epoxide ring from the opposite direction to its oxygen atom: consequently a *trans*-glycol results.

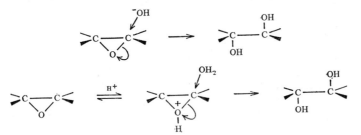

Thus cyclohexene-oxide yields the resolvable cyclohexan-1,2-diol (VII) and the steroid (VI) gives the *trans-di-axial* compound (VIII).

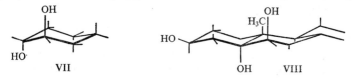

With large rings however transannular interactions of spatially adjacent groups may lead to the formation of some unexpected products, e.g.

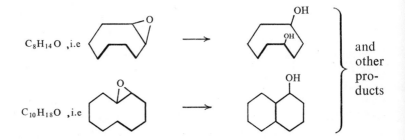

Lithium aluminium hydride is a useful reagent for converting epoxides to monohydric alcohols. This again is a S_N2 reaction which, with the rigid epoxides of steroids and polycyclic terpenes, again gives axial alcohols. Thus (VI) gives (IX).

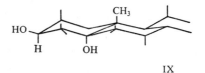

IX

The net result of first treating an olefin with a per-acid and then treating the resulting epoxide with lithium aluminium hydride is not an oxidation but a stereospecific hydration.

Acid and base catalysed decompositions of hydroperoxides

In dilute aqueous acid hydroperoxides which can form reasonably stable carbonium ions may undergo solvolysis (S_N1) to the corresponding alcohol and hydrogen peroxide

$$HO\!-\!O\!-\!CR_3 \rightleftharpoons HO\!-\!O^- + {}^+CR_3 \xrightarrow{H+} HO\!-\!OH + HO\!-\!CR_3$$

and this reaction is used in technical syntheses of hydrogen peroxide from hydroperoxides obtained through autoxidation reactions (see pp. 26–27).

Under conditions that do not favour solvolysis, however, alkyl hydroperoxides are basic enough to be able to add a proton to the hydroxyl group. The molecule then becomes so strongly polarized that O—O fission occurs, together with a concerted molecular re-arrangement that yields a carbonium ion rather than an oxy-cation.

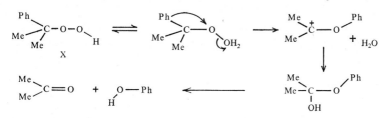

The decomposition of cumene hydroperoxide (X), given above, is now the essential feature of a commercially important synthesis of phenol in which benzene and propylene are first combined together to give cumene which is then autoxidized under neutral conditions.

This acid-catalysed rearrangement of hydroperoxides has a similar mechanism to the pinacol–pinacolone reaction and, in general, the group that migrates from carbon to oxygen is not the group most easily liberated as a free radical in homolytic decompositions of hydro-peroxides, but is the group which has a *trans*-conformation to the hydroxyl.

Many peroxy-esters are sufficiently polar to react in this way on heating without the addition of a catalyst. Criegee, for instance, has shown that esters of decalin-9-hydroperoxide can rearrange as follows when warmed in an ionizing solvent: the reaction affords a convenient way of opening many alicyclic rings.

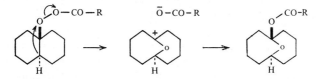

Diacyl peroxides, too, can be decomposed heterolytically in a polar environment and so should never be used as catalysts in mineral acid solution. The introduction of benzoyloxy groups into the nuclei of phenols and the direct oxidation of aromatic amines by benzoyl peroxide are now considered to be heterolytic reactions (see Chapter 9).

The anions of per-acids and of hydroperoxides are reasonably stable in cold dilute alkali, but in concentrated alkali secondary hydroperoxides easily lose water and yield ketones by a base-catalysed elimination (E2), that occurs in competition with bimolecular (S_N2) hydrolysis. With many tertiary alkyl hydroperoxides the latter hydrolysis appears to be linked with oxygen evolution. This has been depicted as a concerted reaction since it occurs most easily when equimolar amounts of a hydroperoxide and its sodium salt are warmed in benzene.

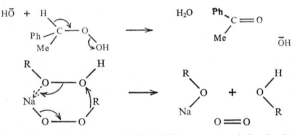

A similar scheme has been used by Wiberg to explain the hydrogen peroxide catalysed hydrolysis of nitriles.

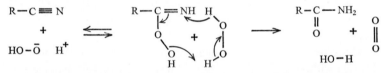

Quite a number of peroxide oxidations involving molecular re-arrangements similar to those of page 45 depend on the ease of separation of a stable anion from an organic peroxide. The most important of these is the oxidative fission of ketones by per-acids. It was first described by Baeyer and Villiger who made use of Caro's acid, H_2SO_5. In this oxidation an acid-catalysed mechanism operates, for the peroxy anion is weakly nucleophilic and so the formation of a carbonium ion at the carbon centre of the ketone is a requisite initial stage. In the final step the O—O bond breaks heterolytically so as to extrude the stable anion $(HSO_4)^-$.

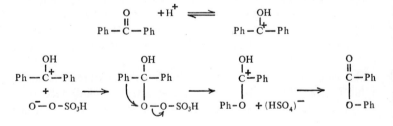

Organic per-acids can be used in place of Caro's acid and the most effective reagent, at present, seems to be per-trifluoroacetic acid, F_3C—CO—O—OH, where again the O—O bond breaks in the final stage so as to give the anion of a strong acid. The reaction has been extended in many ways; for example it is useful for the elimination of acyl groups from steroids and for the fission of cyclic ketones.

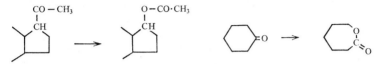

In contrast to this, 1,2-diketones, *ortho*-quinones and α-keto-acids can be oxidized by alkaline hydrogen peroxide and not easily by free per-acids. The initial step here is the addition of the (H—O—O)⁻ anion to a carbonyl group at which the natural electrophilic character of the carbon centre has been enhanced by the polar effect of a similar vicinal group and the adduct can then become stabilized by C—C fission. These oxidations are all smooth, quantitative processes.

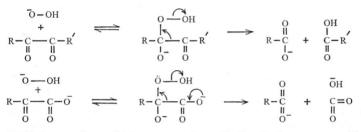

Dakin's reaction, which occurs when alkaline hydrogen peroxide is added to a phenolic aldehyde or ketone, is clearly another example

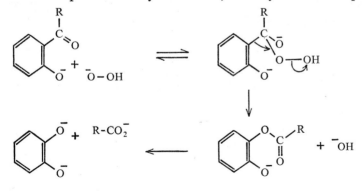

of the same general type and it illustrates the ease of migration of an aryl group from carbon to oxygen.

In parallel with the α-keto-acids, $\alpha\beta$-unsaturated ketones are not attacked by per-acids, for the C=C bond is then of electrophilic and not of nucleophilic character. Consequently they react with alkaline hydrogen peroxide, and eventually yield keto-epoxides, just as they will add other active anions, such as (CN)$^-$ to the C=C bond.

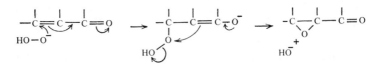

Epoxides of quinones can be made in a similar way, and the oxidation is also an effective route for the controlled degradation of flavones.

General reading references (*additional to previous chapter*)

DAVIES, A. G., *Organic Peroxides*, Butterworths, London, 1961.

FIESER, L. F. and FIESER, M., *Advanced Organic Chemistry*, Reinhold Publishing Corporation, New York, 1962.

GRAY, P. and WILLIAMS, A., *Chemical Reviews*, 1959, **59**, 304 (Alkyloxy radicals).

WATERS, W. A., 'Homolytic Oxidation Processes', In *Progress in Organic Chemistry*, Vol. 5. Butterworths, London, 1961.

CHAPTER 4

The Oxidation of Alcohols

Primary and secondary alcohols are oxidized much more readily than paraffin hydrocarbons or ethers, whilst tertiary alcohols are quite difficult to oxidize, especially by heterolytic reagents. It follows therefore that oxidations of the type

$$H—\overset{|}{\underset{|}{C}}—OH \longrightarrow \overset{|}{C}{=}O$$

must occur either by a series of facile reactions, in which the OH group is first concerned, or by a concerted process in which both the C—H and O—H groups are severed together.

Homolytic oxidation of alcohols

Direct oxidation by hydroxyl radicals, described in Chapter 3, is a chain reaction for primary and secondary alcohols and involves $R_2\overset{\cdot}{C}$—OH radicals; for tertiary alcohols a more distant C—H group is attacked and the oxidation is no longer a chain process.

For other homolytic oxidations of alcohols the appropriate model reaction is the formation and breakdown of an alkyl hydroperoxide (pp. 33–40). Thus nitric, nitrous and hypochlorous acids react by giving esters, R.O.X, that break down either because the O—X bond is weak, like the O—O bond of peroxides, or because •X can separate as a stable free radical, such as NO or NO_2.

1. $\qquad ROH + HOCl \rightleftharpoons ROCl \qquad \longrightarrow RO\cdot + \cdot Cl$

2. $\qquad ROH + HNO_3 \rightleftharpoons RO—NO_2 \longrightarrow RO\cdot + NO_2$

3. $\qquad ROH + HNO_2 \rightleftharpoons RO—NO \longrightarrow RO\cdot + NO$

The subsequent breakdown of the alkyloxy radical, to give a more active alkyl radical, and secondary reactions involving the inorganic fragments (•Cl, NO_2, etc.) can lead to very extensive oxidative degradations.

In the case of tertiary alkyl hypochlorites the initial homolysis leads to a controllable long-chain reaction from which simple products can be obtained in good yield, e.g.

4. $Me_3C—O—Cl$ $\longrightarrow$ $Me_3C—O\cdot + \cdot Cl$
5. $Me_3C—O\cdot$ $\longrightarrow$ $Me_2C=O + \cdot Me$
6. $Me_3C—O—Cl + \cdot Me$ $\longrightarrow$ $Me_3C—O + \cdot Me—Cl$

but if this reaction is carried out in a hydrocarbon solvent then the alkyl radicals may preferentially attack the solvent. This trouble can be obviated by using a halogenated solvent such as carbon tetrachloride. Though the cleavage reaction (5), which leads to the formation of an alkyl chloride (6), always occurs, Walling and Padwa (*J.A.C.S.* 1961, **83**, 2207) have shown that at moderate temperatures hydrogen abstraction can occur at the fourth carbon atom of a long chain hypochlorite and is the main reaction even in fairly dilute solution, giving yields of up to 80%. For example

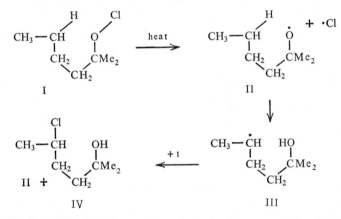

The 1,4-chlorohydrins, such as (IV) can be converted into tetrahydrofuran derivatives by treatment with alcoholic potassium hydroxide. A similar reaction has been effected photochemically in benzene solution with a steroid (*J.A.C.S.* 1961, **83**, 2213),

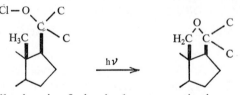

whilst the following ring fission is almost quantitative.

Primary and secondary hypochlorites decompose so rapidly at room temperature that they cannot be used for controllable oxidations.

The homolytic decomposition of *alkyl nitrates*, which may occur in oxidations of organic compounds by concentrated nitric acid, involves very complicated and often explosive reaction sequences which are not fully understood. Following the decomposition of an alkyloxy radical, (5), nitrogen dioxide may combine with an alkyl radical to give either a nitroparaffin (7) or an alkyl nitrite (8), but the latter reaction leads almost immediately to further degradation, for a new alkyloxy radical can rapidly be formed (see Gray and Williams, *Chem. Reviews*, 1959, **59**, 304).

7. $R \cdot + NO_2 \longrightarrow R{-}NO_2$

8. $R \cdot + NO_2 \longrightarrow R{-}O{-}NO \longrightarrow RO \cdot + NO$

Thus reaction (8) is a chain propagating process. Again, nitroparaffins are very easily dehydrogenated and so do not survive as major reaction products.

The thermal decomposition of *alkyl nitrites* mainly yields aldehydes or ketones and was originally thought to follow the simple course typified by the decomposition of benzyl nitrite

9. $Ph{-}CH_2{-}O{-}NO \longrightarrow Ph{-}CH_2{-}O \cdot + NO$

10. $Ph{-}CH_2{-}O \cdot + Ph{-}CH_2{-}O{-}NO$
$$\longrightarrow Ph{-}CH_2{-}OH + Ph{-}\overset{\cdot}{C}H{-}O{-}NO$$

11. $Ph{-}\overset{\cdot}{C}H{-}O{-}NO \longrightarrow Ph{-}CH{=}O + NO$

but this is a simplification of the general reaction picture, for with other nitrites the usual homolytic decomposition of an alkyloxy radical (reaction 5) can also occur and the final mixture of products contains both nitrous oxide and nitrogen gases. By analogy with gas phase studies of pyrolyses of nitrites the formation of nitrous oxide has been attributed to the reactions (12) and (13) (see Gray *et al., J. Chem. Soc.* 1961, 2620, 4006):

12. $R{-}CH_2{-}O \cdot + NO \longrightarrow R{-}CH{=}O + HNO$

13. $2HNO \longrightarrow N_2O + H_2O$

Reaction (12), the abstraction of hydrogen from a radical by nitric oxide, should be exothermic and so can rationally be postulated, but a reaction such as (14)

14. $R—CH_2—OH + NO \longrightarrow R—\overset{\cdot}{C}H—OH + HNO$

would be endothermic and so does not occur. Reactions (11) and (12) destroy active radicals and so the homolytic decomposition of nitrites is *not* a chain reaction.

However alkyl nitrites do not undergo appreciable thermal decomposition below 150°, and, since most solvents for them are attacked by alkyl or alkyloxy radicals at this high temperature, the thermal fission of nitrites is not a very practicable route of alcohol oxidation. Compounds which decompose homolytically can all be decomposed photochemically at room temperature provided that they have absorption bands at wave-lengths suitable for irradiation, and in 1960 D. H. R. Barton showed that in the steroid series the alkyloxy radicals formed by the homolysis of nitrites could react intramolecularly and thereby he effected the following novel synthesis of aldosterone acetate (see P. de Mayo and D. T. Reid, *Chem. Soc. Quart. Reviews*, 1961, **15**, 397).

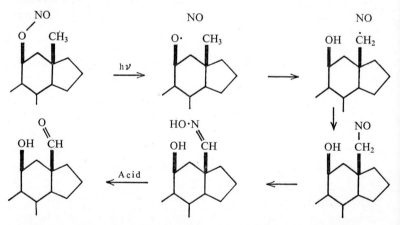

The conditions for effecting this intramolecular '*Barton reaction*' have now been investigated in some detail (*J.A.C.S.* 1962, **84**, 2711–2726), and it has been shown that in the photolysis of octyl nitrite the transient octyloxy radical (V) specifically attacks the —CH₂— group at position *4* in the hydrocarbon chain, giving an alkyl radical (VI)

that recombines with nitric oxide giving a product (VII) which was isolated in the form of its dimer. (The general formula for the dimeric nitroso-compounds is (VIII).

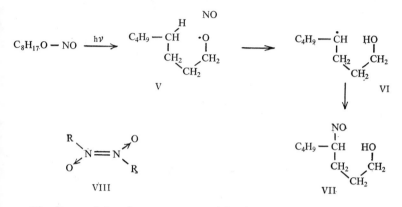

The dimer of the nitroso-compound (VII) was isolated in 45% yield when the decomposition was carried out in benzene, together with 25% of 1-octanol and 15% of 1-octanal, formed by reactions (10) and (11) of p. 51, but in heptane solution the octyloxy radicals also attacked the solvent and the dimers of 2-, 3-, and 4-nitrosoheptane were formed as well.

Similarly the photolysis of o-methylbenzyl nitrite (IX) gave the dimer of (X). Thus in all cases the transition state of the intramolecular hydrogen transfer has a 6-membered ring.

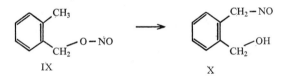

The dimeric nitroso-compounds can easily be isolated from reactions carried out in hydrocarbon solvents, but they slowly isomerize to oximes. The latter reaction is heterolytic and is favoured by the use of polar solvents which are not the best media to use for effecting photochemical reactions.

In a similar way azides may be cyclized either thermally or photochemically with extrusion of nitrogen (G. Smolinsky, *J.A.C.S.* 1960, **82**, 4717; 1961, **83**, 2489) and again this reaction may be used for natural product synthesis (Barton and Morgan, *J. Chem. Soc.* 1962, 622).

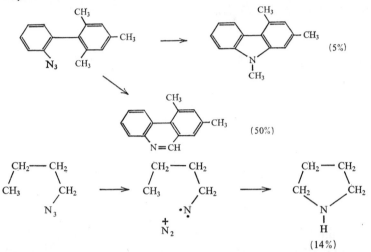

The latter reaction is very similar in mechanism to the cyclization of aliphatic amines which can be effected by oxidation with chlorine or bromine and has been shown to be a homolytic process that proceeds through intermediate N-halogen compounds. This cyclization can be effected both by the action of light and by reducing agents such as ferrous salts. (Wawzonek and Thelen, *J.A.C.S.* 1950, **72**, 2118: Corey and Hertler, *ibid.* 1960, **82**, 1657.)

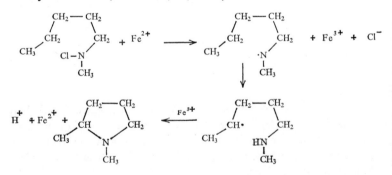

Oxidation by ions of the transition metals
Monohydric alcohols are attacked slowly by those ions of transition metals which have high redox potentials ($E_0 > 1 \cdot 2$ V), i.e. V^V, Ce^{IV},

Co^{III}, Mn^{III}. These ions are all solvated in solution, and water molecules or other ligand groups fill the co-ordination shell around the metal atoms. Inorganic isotope exchange reactions show that oxidations and reductions of these ions often occur by atom transfer between ligands rather than by direct electron transfer (see *Faraday Soc. Discussion*, 1960, **29**) and the reduction of the metallic ion to its lower valency can involve the participation of a ligand group. Saffir and Taube (*J.A.C.S.* 1960, **82**, 13), for instance, have shown that ammonocobaltic oxalate and ceric perchlorate react together as follows:

15. $\{(NH_3)_5Co-C_2O_4H\}^+ + Ce^{IV} \longrightarrow Co^{II} + Ce^{III} + 2CO_2 + 5NH_4^+$

the oxalate group giving one electron to the ceric ion and the other to the cobalt.

For this reason it would be anticipated that the one-electron oxidation of an alcohol in aqueous solution should be an electron transfer process (17) following the rapid, reversible, formation of an initial complex, e.g.

16. $R_3C-OH + \{Co(H_2O)_6\}^{3+} \rightleftharpoons \left\{\begin{array}{c} R_3C-O \rightarrow Co(H_2O)_5 \\ | \\ H \end{array}\right\}^{3+} + H_2O$

17. $\underset{\underset{H}{\overset{|}{}}}{R_3C-O} \overset{}{-\!\!\!\!\cdots\overset{III}{Co}(H_2O)_5} \longrightarrow R_3C-O\cdot \;+\; Co^{II}_{aq} \;+\; H^+$

With ions of Ce^{IV} and V^V, immediate colour changes on admixture with alcohols show that complex ions are indeed formed.

Reaction (17) should yield an alkyloxy radical, but it has been found that (i) primary and secondary alcohols are oxidized more easily than are many tertiary alcohols, and (ii) that the replacement of CH(OH) by CD(OH) often reduces the reaction rate. Consequently the rate-determining stage in the oxidation of primary and secondary alcohols by ions of the transition metals must involve, to some extent, the breaking of C—H bonds.

In the case of the oxidation of cyclohexanol by quinquevalent vanadium the course of the reaction has been worked out by a kinetic study (Littler and Waters, *J. Chem. Soc.* 1959, 4046). Oxidation by vanadium-(V) is associated with its yellow cations, VO_2^+, aq. and $\{V(OH)_3\}^{2+}$ which are formed in mineral acid solution and are easily reduced to the blue vanadyl cation, $(VO)^{2+}$, of quadrivalent vanadium.

The vanadic ion, V^{3+}, which is a strong reducing agent, is not involved in oxidations of organic compounds by vanadium-(V), e.g.

18. $V^V + R_2CH(OH) \longrightarrow V^{III} + R_2C=O + 2H^+$ (*heterolytic*)

19. $V^{III} + V^V \longrightarrow 2V^{IV}$ (*very rapid*)

because the oxidations yield transient organic free radicals which can initiate the polymerisation of acrylonitrile and can be detected as end-groups in the resulting polymers.

   Now, in both sulphuric and perchloric acid solutions of constant ionic strength, oxidation of cyclohexanol by vanadium-(V) is an acid catalysed reaction with a rate proportional to the hydrogen ion *concentration* and not to the hydrogen ion activity (which is measured by Hammett's acidity function, h_o), and also is of first order with respect to both [cyclohexanol] and [V^V]. Consequently the slow reaction involves a complex of the alcohol, vanadium-(V), a proton and a water molecule. The equations of the type of (16 and 17) must therefore be expanded to:

20. $VO_2^+ + H_3O^+ \rightleftharpoons \{V(OH)_3\}^{2+}$ (*fast*)

21. $R_2CH(OH) + \{V(OH)_3\}^{2+} \underset{\text{fast}}{\rightleftharpoons} \text{(Complex)} \overset{\text{slow}}{\longrightarrow}$ Products

and since replacement of cyclohexanol by 1-deuterocyclohexanol reduces the oxidation rate (k_H/k_D *ca.* 4) it must be concluded that the oxidation involves the concerted reaction shown below, in which a carbon radical (XI) rather than an alkyloxy radical is formed.

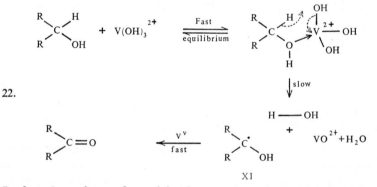

22.

XI

In fact the polymer formed in the presence of acrylonitrile does contain hydroxyl groups.

23. $R_2\dot{C}{-}OH + CH_2{=}CH{-}CN \longrightarrow R_2C(OH){-}CH_2{-}CH(CN){-}$

However, some oxidations with quinquevalent vanadium do show reactivity typical of alkyloxy radical formation. For instance C—C fission rather than C—H fission occurs in the oxidations of both β-phenyl-ethanol and of α-phenyl-tertiarybutyl carbinol, Ph—CH(OH)—CMe$_3$.

$$Ph-CH_2-CH_2-OH \longrightarrow Ph-CH_2-CH_2-\overset{\displaystyle O}{\underset{\displaystyle H}{|}}-V(OH)_3{}^{2+}$$

$$\downarrow$$

$$Ph-CH=O + H-CO_2H \longleftarrow Ph-CH_2\cdot + CH_2=O + V^{IV}$$

These oxidations clearly take the path requiring the least activation energy, for the radical Ph—CH$_2$· is resonance-stabilized to a much greater extent than would be the radical Ph—CH$_2$—$\overset{\cdot}{\text{C}}$H—OH resulting from C—H fission.

Definite, though much smaller (k_H/k_D, 1·6–2·0) kinetic isotope effects have been measured for oxidations of cyclohexanol by ceric, manganic and cobaltic ions in highly acidic solutions, so that with these more powerful oxidants the reaction process much more nearly resembles equation (17) in which an alkyloxy radical is formed. Actually with cobaltic perchlorate, which has a very high redox potential (E_0, 1·8 V), even tertiary alcohols can be oxidized to products which clearly arise from the slow formation and rapid breakdown of alkyloxy radicals (Hoare and Waters, *J. Chem. Soc.* 1962, 965). The cobaltic ion, which is slowly reduced even by water, can be stabilized by the use of concentrated mineral acid and oxidations by Co^{III} show an inverse acidity dependence that can be correlated with the equilibrium,

24. $\quad \{Co(H_2O)_6\}^{3+} + H_2O \rightleftharpoons \{HO—Co(H_2O)_5\}^{2+} + H_3O^+$
$\qquad$ *weaker oxidant* $\qquad\qquad$ *stronger oxidant*

and again the oxidation of an alcohol presumably involves a preliminary rapid displacement of co-ordinated water, or hydroxyl, by an alcohol molecule.

In the case of the oxidation of diethyl carbinol, Et$_2$CH—OH, by cobaltic perchlorate, C—C fission preponderates and the kinetic isotope effect becomes negligibly small. Thus this oxidation corresponds fairly closely to a reaction involving the slow formation of the

5

free secondary alkyloxy radical, Et_2CH—O• (Hoare and Waters, in press 1963).

In solvents other than water, e.g. acetic acid, other molecules are co-ordinated with the metallic ion and these changes naturally effect equilibria such as (22) or (24), redox potentials and also chemical reactivity.

Heterolytic oxidations of alcohols

These are all elimination reactions in which the hydrogen atom of the C—H bond is removed, together with a pair of electrons. In some cases the oxidation resembles the base-catalysed decomposition of a hydroperoxide (p. 46) in that the oxidant is initially attached to the oxygen atom of the alcohol, i.e.

A.

$$B:+H—C—O—Ox \longrightarrow (BH)^+ + C\!\!=\!\!O + Ox^-$$

but the electron movement may occur in the reverse direction and is then termed a 'hydride transfer',

B.

$$Ox+H—C—O—H \longrightarrow Ox—H + C\!\!=\!\!O + H^+$$

and in many cases these electron movements occur within a cyclic intermediate, or transition, complex. For all these oxidations one can, by replacing the C—H group of the alcohol by a C—D group which requires more energy for its rupture, show that the fission of the C—H bond is part of the rate-determining oxidation process: the deuterated compound is oxidized more slowly. Interpretation of the magnitudes of these kinetic isotope effects (k_H/k_D) however is still controversial.

The base-catalysed reaction of equation (A) is known to occur with nitrate esters, which eliminate $(NO_2)^-$, and with hypochlorites, but far more significantly it is an essential feature of the oxidation of alcohols by *chromic acid*. Our knowledge of the mechanism of this reaction is mainly due to the kinetic studies of F. H. Westheimer and his colleagues on the oxidation of isopropanol, which have been of outstanding importance in the elucidation of the mechanisms of all oxidations of organic compounds by this important reagent, and therefore merit consideration in some detail (for references see W. A. Waters, *Chem. Soc. Quart. Reviews*, 1958, **12**, 277).

The reduction of chromic acid to a chromic salt by an organic compound must necessarily occur in stages since the overall valency change from Cr^{VI} to Cr^{III} involves the movement to an inner shell of three valency electrons, i.e. more than can be provided by the rupture of any covalence. In the oxidation of isopropanol the rate-determining reaction undoubtedly involves the reduction of Cr^{VI} to an unstable ion of Cr^{IV}, since if the oxidation is carried out in the presence of a manganous salt then manganese dioxide is formed in an amount equivalent to one-third of the oxidizing power of the initial chromate, although chromic acid itself does not oxidize manganous ions. Hence one may write:

25. $Cr^{VI} + Me_2CH-OH \longrightarrow Cr^{IV} + Me_2C{=}O + 2H^+$ (*slow*)

26. $Cr^{IV} + Mn^{2+} \longrightarrow Cr^{III} + Mn^{3+}$

27. $2Mn^{3+} + 2H_2O \longrightarrow MnO_2 + Mn^{2+} + 4H^+$ } (*both fast*)

Cerous salts (Ce^{III}) behave in the same way as manganous salts, and in *dilute* mineral acid ceric salts do not oxidize alcohols at an appreciable rate.

If manganous or cerous salts are present in excess then the initial rate of oxidation of isopropanol by chromic acid is reduced by about 50% and hence Westheimer concluded that in the absence of manganous ions the following fast reactions occur, the oxidation of the isopropanol being regarded entirely as a two-electron transfer.

28. $Cr^{IV} + Cr^{VI} \longrightarrow 2Cr^{V}$

29. $Cr^{V} + Me_2CH-OH \longrightarrow Cr^{III} + Me_2C{=}O + 2H^+$

Even yet very little is known about the nature and chemical properties of the ions formed in aqueous acid from either Cr^V or Cr^{IV}, for their lifetimes are too short for their study by spectroscopic methods.

A further complication concerning chromic acid oxidations is the fact that many different ionic species of Cr^{VI} can exist in solution. The neutral chromate ion, $(CrO_4)^{2-}$, has no oxidizing power, and in aqueous solution the bichromate ion, $(Cr_2O_7)^{2-}$, formed by the rapid equilibrium,

30. $2(HCrO_4)^- \rightleftharpoons (Cr_2O_7)^{2-} + H_2O$

which prevents the use of the ^{18}O-labelling technique in following reactions of chromates, has an oxidizing power that is negligible in comparison with that of the acid chromate ion $(HCrO_4)^-$. Thus the relative rate of alcohol oxidations by aqueous chromic acid increases as the concentration of the chromic acid decreases, for the equilibrium

(30) then shifts to the left. Again, chloride ions decrease the oxidizing power of chromic acid solutions, for the chlorochromate anion $(Cl.CrO_3)^-$ is a much weaker oxidizer than $(HCrO_4)^-$. However, acetic acid increases the oxidizing power of chromic acid; the oxidation of isopropanol in 86·5% acetic acid proceeds 2500 times faster than in water at the same hydrogen ion concentration. This may perhaps be due to the formation of a highly active acetyl-chromate anion, $(CH_3.CO.O.CrO_3)^-$.

Chromium trioxide in glacial acetic acid is a particularly complex medium for kinetic study, for it corresponds to a minimum solubility point in the CrO_3—H_2O—$(CH_3.CO)_2O$ system and undoubtedly contains some diacetyl chromate, $CrO_2(O.CO.CH_3)_2$. Again, unless free mineral acid is added, oxidations effected with chromium trioxide in glacial acetic acid produce Cr^{III} cations which immediately buffer the system, reducing the hydrogen ion concentration and with it the oxidation rate; there even may be deposited sparingly soluble chromic chromates, or complex salts, such as Cr^{III} $(HCrO_4)$ $(O.CO.CH_3)_2$. Moreover there is evidence that in acetic anhydride compounds of chromium-(IV) become much more stable.

Both in water and in aqueous acetic acid the rate of oxidation of isopropanol by chromic acid is directly proportional to the alcohol concentration. In water the oxidation rate in moderately acid (0·2 molar and upward) solution is proportional to the *square* of the hydrogen ion concentration, but it becomes closely proportional to the first power of the hydrogen ion concentration at lower acidities, whilst in 86·5% acetic acid solutions of pH < 1 the rate is strictly proportional to the acidity. From this evidence Westheimer concluded that the slow oxidation step in the whole reaction process was preceded by a fast, reversible, esterification capable of acid catalysis,

31. $(HCrO_4)^- + H_3O^+ \rightleftharpoons H_2CrO_4 + H_2O$

32. Me_2CH—$OH + H_2CrO_4 \rightleftharpoons Me_2CH$—$O$—$CrO_2$—$OH + H_2O$

33. Me_2CH—$OH + H_2CrO_4 + H^+ \rightleftharpoons (Me_2CH$—$O$—$CrO_3H_2)^+ + H_2O$

and found that, by extraction with benzene, *di*-isopropyl chromate could be extracted from cold chromic acid–isopropanol mixtures.

Further evidence concerning the nature of the reacting species in acid catalysed reactions can be obtained by the study of *solvent isotope effects*. Heavy water, D_2O, is a slightly weaker base than ordinary water, H_2O, but the protonated molecules, HD_2O^+ and H_3O^+, are acids of comparable strength. Hence for any partly dissociated acid the equilibria for the reactions

34. $$H—A + H_2O \underset{\xleftarrow{\hspace{1cm}}}{\overset{K_{H_2O}}{\xrightarrow{\hspace{1cm}}}} H_3O^+ + A^-$$

35. $$H—A + D_2O \underset{\xleftarrow{\hspace{1cm}}}{\overset{K_{D_2O}}{\xrightarrow{\hspace{1cm}}}} HD_2O^+ + A^- \underset{\xleftarrow{\hspace{1cm}}}{\xrightarrow{\hspace{1cm}}} D—A + HDO$$

are different, there being more undissociated acid present in D_2O than in H_2O. The value of the ratio K_{H_2O}/K_{D_2O} rises gradually from about 2 for a mineral acid, such as sulphuric acid, to 3·3 for acetic acid and about 4 for a phenol (see R. P. Bell, *The Proton in Chemistry*, Chap. XI, Methuen, 1960).

Now the equilibrium

31. $$H_2O + H_2CrO_4 \underset{\xleftarrow{\hspace{1cm}}}{\xrightarrow{\hspace{1cm}}} H_3O^+ + HCrO_4^-$$

will alter in heavy water so that more undissociated H_2CrO_4 is present, and this in turn will affect equilibrium (32) so as to favour the formation of the ester $Me_2CH—O—CrO_2—OH$. Thus if the rate of oxidation of isopropanol is to be measured by the rate of decomposition of this ester then the reaction should occur more rapidly in D_2O than in H_2O.

The solvent isotope effect found for slow oxidations carried out in very dilute acid, k_{D_2O}/k_{H_2O}, is 2·44 which is appropriate for an acid with the dissociation constant of chromic acid ($K_1 = 0·18$). For faster oxidations effected in stronger acid, when the reaction is of second order with respect to the acidity, k_{D_2O}/k_{H_2O} rises to a value of over 6, so that *two* acid-base equilibria, corresponding to that of equation (33), are then involved.

In 1949 Oppenauer and Oberrauch introduced *tertiary butyl chromate* as a specific oxidizer for primary and secondary alcohols in acetic acid, or acetic acid–benzene mixtures. It has been shown that this reagent acts by a rapid trans-esterification which involves electron-pair displacements at the chromium atom, since with an isotopically labelled alcohol, $R—^{18}O—H$ there is no loss of ^{18}O to the solvent on hydrolysis of the chromate ester, and with an optically active alcohol there is no racemization.

In aqueous solution the rate of oxidation of 2-deuteroiso-propanol, $Me_2CD—OH$, is about $\frac{1}{7}$ of the rate of oxidation of either the ordinary alcohol, $Me_2CH—OH$, or of the alcohol $(D_3C)_2CH—OH$, and hence

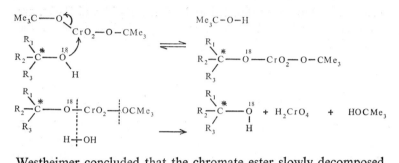

Westheimer concluded that the chromate ester slowly decomposed by the base-catalysed elimination route A of p. 58, with the solvent, water, acting as the base.

Mere traces of bases markedly catalyse the breakdown of non-aqueous solutions of chromate esters and indeed the decomposition of di-isopropyl chromate in benzene containing pyridine is a first-order process with respect to both the ester and the pyridine. In this connection it may be noted that a solution of chromium trioxide in anhydrous pyridine may be used for the specific oxidation of sparingly soluble alcohols. However, the cogency of a base-catalysed elimination in a strongly acid environment has been questioned on the basis of kinetic evidence, and under these (the normal) reaction conditions it is probable that the oxidation step has a cyclic mechanism in which again the oxygen atom of the final ketone is the oxygen atom of the original alcohol.

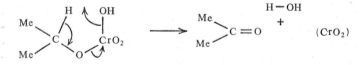

The cyclic oxidation mechanism could alternatively be formulated as a hydride transfer (B, p. 58) by mere reversal of the arrows in the above diagram and this indeed has been proposed.

However, it is not rational to formulate the oxidation of isopropanol as a *direct* hydride transfer not involving a previous esterification, for were this to be the case then the oxidation would proceed more slowly in D_2O than in H_2O, since the rate-determining process would then involve the breaking of either an O—H or an O—D bond, so that there should be a primary kinetic isotope effect.

In 1950 D. H. R. Barton pointed out that of the rigid secondary alcohols of the steroid series those with axially oriented OH groups and equatorial C—H were oxidized more rapidly than their epimers and explained this by Westheimer's theory that the solvolytic reaction was the rate-controlling process, for equatorial hydrogens should be the more accessible for solvent attack than the stereochemically less accessible axial hydrogens.

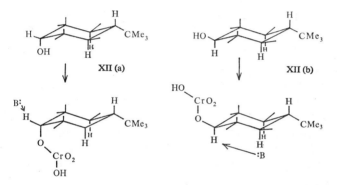

Though this view has been supported by rate measurements with the epimeric alcohols XII (a) and XII (b), it is equally evident that the esterification of an axial O—H should not be as easy as that of an equatorial O—H and so the steric hindrance rule is no more than an empirical guide. It has recently been shown (*Helv. Chim. Acta*, 1962, **45**, 2554) that with a highly sterically hindered secondary alcohol the initial esterification does indeed become the rate-determining process. When this is the case the replacement of CH(OH) by CD(OH) has no effect on the oxidation rate.

Some evidence concerning the later stages of chromic acid oxidation of alcohols is now emerging. Firstly, the kinetic isotope effect in isopropanol oxidation varies with the solvent employed and is not exactly the same if measured for initial reaction velocities and for nearly completed reactions (L. Kaplan, *J.A.C.S.* 1955, 77, 5469), so that the oxidation by Cr^V (p. 59) may not be exactly similar to that by Cr^{VI}. Again, some C—C bond fission cleavage occurs during chromic acid oxidations of certain alcohols, as for example α-tert. butyl benzyl alcohol:

$$Ph.CH(OH)CMe_3 \longrightarrow Ph.CO.CMe_3 \quad and \quad Ph.CHO + HO.CMe_3$$

The extent of C—C cleavage may be reduced sharply by adding manganous or cerous ions so as to remove any Cr^{IV} intermediate as soon as it is formed. It has been suggested that the C—C cleavage is an oxidation by Cr^V, but, as mentioned on p. 57, reactions of exactly this type have been observed in the homolytic oxidation of alcohols by vanadium-V, and so reaction sequences such as

36. $Cr^{IV} + Ph—CH—CMe_3 \longrightarrow Cr^{III} + Ph—CH—CMe_3$
        (or Cr^V) | (or Cr^{IV}) |
                         O—H   O·

37. $Ph—CH—CMe_3 \longrightarrow Ph—CH + ·CMe_3$
            | ‖
            O·   O

38. $Cr^{VI} + ·CMe_3 + H_2O \longrightarrow Cr^V + HO—CMe_3 + H^+$

can tentatively be proposed.

Homolytic oxidations such as (36) evidently do not take place with Cr^{VI}, for if so tertiary alcohols should be more prone to oxidation by chromic acid than is the case. Tertiary alcohols can indeed be oxidized by chromic acid–sulphuric acid mixtures, but it has been shown that these reactions are of zero order with respect to the chromic acid and that the rate-determining step is the dehydration of the alcohol to the olefin.

39. $(C_2H_5)_3C—OH \xrightarrow[(H^+)]{} (C_2H_5)_2C{=}CH—CH_3$

A good example of alcohol oxidation by the proton elimination mechanism, A, has been described by Kornblum and his colleagues (*J.A.C.S.* 1957, **79**, 6562; 1959, **81**, 4113) who have shown that alkyl tosylates, and phenacyl halides, can be converted to aldehydes by warming with *dimethylsulphoxide* and sodium bicarbonate. Here a slow electrophilic displacement at the carbon centre of the alcohol is followed by an elimination which reduces the sulphoxide to sulphide.

Since the oxygen atom of the sulphoxide is a poor nucleophilic reagent it is necessary to select an alcohol derivative with a good leaving group.

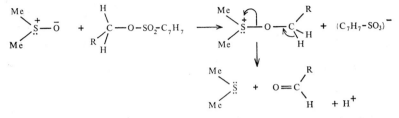

Oxygen transfers of the reverse type can occur with organic phosphines or phosphites, e.g.

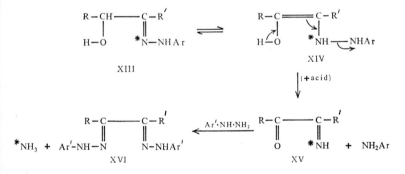

and from other compounds of elements of groups V and VI which, like sulphoxides, have an oxygen atom bound by a semi-polar bond and not by a double covalence as in ketones.

Another interesting example of the oxidation of a CH(OH) group by the proton elimination, A, is *the conversion of an acyloin, such as glucose, to an osazone* by treatment with phenylhydrazine, a compound which in all other reactions is a reducing rather than an oxidizing agent. By the use of a ^{15}N-labelled phenylhydrazine it has been shown (*Chem. & Ind.* 1959, 1195) that the oxidation is really an elimination reaction of the intermediate phenylhydrazone (XIII), since if an isotopically labelled phenylhydrazone is treated with more unlabelled phenylhydrazine then the ^{15}N is displaced as the osazone forms.

Conversion of (XIII) to (XIV) is a simple tautomeric change and the real oxidation is the formation of (XV) from (XIV). In this step an arylamine, Ar.NH_2, is decidedly more basic than a hydrazine, R.NH—NH.Ar, and so the N—N bond breaks in the presence of even a weak acid. The conditions for the cleavage are similar to those required for both the benzidine and Fischer's indole rearrangements.

Quite similar in mechanism to this acyloin oxidation are the reactions involved in the biological oxidations of α-amino-acids in which vitamin B_6 (pyridoxal pyrophosphate) plays a part; these can be simulated by several model systems. Aldehydes and many ketones condense easily with α-amino-acids giving imines. If the product contains an electron-attracting group, such as an adjacent C=O, as in ninhydrin or isatin, or the conjugated nitrogen atom of a heterocyclic base, then the adduct is easily decarboxylated by an acid-catalysed reaction.

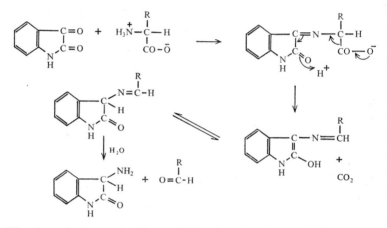

The above is Langenbeck's model for decarboxylase oxidation.

However, with vitamin B_6 in the presence of a metallic ion, such as Cu^{2+}, Fe^{3+} or Al^{3+}, the carboxyl group is held more firmly in the adduct as a chelate complex, so that the C—H bond is severed instead. The reverse of the amino-acid oxidase action shown above occurs biologically in trans-amination (see the diagram on p. 67). (For references, see S. G. Waley, *Mechanisms of Organic and Enzymic Reactions*, Clarendon Press, Oxford, 1962.)

Hydride transfer, B, now seems to be the general route for the heterolytic oxidation of alcohols by reagents which cannot react by way of esterification. A clear-cut example which has been studied kinetically by Bartlett and McCollum (*J.A.C.S.* 1956, **78**, 1441) is the

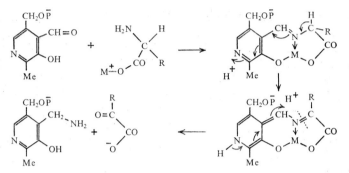

oxidation of an alcohol by a triarylcarbonium ion which occurs in mineral acid solution and is of first order with respect to the triaryl carbinol.

40. $\quad Ph_3C$——OH $\quad + \quad H_3O^+ \quad \rightleftharpoons \quad Ph_3\overset{+}{C} \quad + \quad 2H_2O$

41. $\quad Ph_3\overset{+}{C} \quad + \quad H$—$CMe_2$—O—H $\quad \longrightarrow \quad Ph_3C$—H $\quad + \quad Me_2C$=O $\quad + \quad \overset{+}{H}$

In strong perchloric acid, diarylcarbinols disproportionate by a similar reaction:

42. $\qquad Ph_2CH^+ + H$—CPh_2—O—H $\longrightarrow Ph_2CH_2 + Ph_2C$=O

and with aluminium trichloride as the catalyst even ether can be oxidized by triphenylmethyl chloride.

A deuterated alcohol, e.g. D—CMe_2—OH, transfers deuterium from the D—C bond, but the kinetic isotope effect is rather small ($k_H/k_D = 2\cdot6$) and Swain (*J.A.C.S.* 1961, **83**, 1945) has suggested on theoretical grounds that hydride transfers, B, should exhibit much smaller kinetic isotope effects than proton transfers, A. For this reason the oxidation of alcohols by aqueous *bromine* has been represented as a hydride transfer (43)

43.
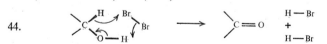

but this can well be a concerted cyclic reaction (Barker, Overend and Rees, *Chem. & Ind.*, 1961, 558)

44.

and since with this model the breaking of the C—H bond involves both bending and stretching it would be expected to show only a small kinetic isotope effect (see R. P. Bell, *The Proton in Chemistry*, Chap. XI, Methuen, 1960). The kinetics of all oxidations by molecular bromine are complicated because bromide anions, as they are formed, remove an equivalent of bromine as the inactive complex anion Br_3^-, but this can be overcome by using a *bromate* as the oxidizer. Again bromine rapidly substitutes the resulting aldehydes or ketones. It has been shown that in acid solution the initial rate of oxidation of ethanol is independent both of the acidity and of the bromide ion concentration, so that the alternative mechanism of oxidation via a reversible oxidation to a hypobromite ester can be rejected.

45. $CH_3—CH_2—OH + Br_2 \rightleftharpoons CH_2—CH_2—O—Br + H^+ + Br^-$

46. $CH_3—CH_2—O—Br \longrightarrow CH_3—CH=O + H—Br$

Again the *permanganate* ion probably oxidizes alcohols by hydride transfer (47), for this second-order reaction can be both acid and base catalysed and there is no evidence for any intermediate ester formation.

47.

$$MnO_4^- \quad + \quad H—\overset{|}{\underset{|}{C}}—O^- \quad \longrightarrow \quad (HMnO_4)^{2-} \quad + \quad \overset{|}{\underset{|}{C}}=O$$

Though one-electron transfer processes, e.g.

48. $H—CR_2—O—H + (MnO_4)^- \longrightarrow H—CR_2—O\cdot + (MnO_4)^{2-} + H^+$

49. $H—CR_2—O\cdot + (MnO_4)^- \longrightarrow CR_2=O + (MnO_4)^{2-} + H^+$

cannot entirely be excluded they are improbable, since in strongly alkaline solution the manganate anion, $(MnO_4)^{2-}$, oxidizes alcohols without giving any sign of forming the transient $(MnO_4)^{3-}$ ion (Pode and Waters, *J. Chem. Soc.* 1956, 3373) and again α-tert. butyl benzyl alcohol, $Ph.CH(OH).CMe_3$, is oxidized to the ketone, $Ph.CO.CMe_3$, without any accompanying C—C fission (see p. 57). However it has been found by R. Stewart (*Faraday Soc. Discussion*, 1960, **29**, 211) that alcohols, such as $Ar.CH(OH).CF_3$, containing powerful electron-attracting substituents give some extraordinary high kinetic isotope effects (k_H/k_D over 16). Some of these are 2—3 times the theoretical maximum calculated from the zero-point-energy difference between C—H and C—D bonds and until these observations can be given a satisfactory theoretical interpretation the quantitative significance of any kinetic isotope studies is doubtful.

In general, mechanisms of permanganate oxidation are even more difficult to interpret from kinetic data than are mechanisms of chromic acid oxidation, because the stable inorganic end-products, Mn^{2+} in acid solution and MnO_2 in alkali, result from rapid secondary reactions of the Mn^V or Mn^{VI} ion that is first formed from the permanganate. The ions $(MnO_4)^{2-}$ and $(MnO_4)^{3-}$, though known, are stable only in exceedingly strong alkali, whilst $(MnO_3)^-$, another possibility, is known only in crystal structures. There is no doubt now but that in mineral acid solution many of the oxidations effected by permanganate are actually due to the manganic ion, Mn^{3+}, but the reactivity of this ion can be diminished greatly by complexing it with pyrophosphate and it is under these conditions that the best evidence for the true reactivity of the $(MnO_4)^-$ ion can be obtained, for though the uncomplexed ion, Mn^{3+}, found in strongly acid (60% H_2SO_4) manganic sulphate solutions, does oxidize primary and secondary alcohols the complex ion of manganic pyrophosphate, $Mn(H_3P_2O_7)_3$, with three pyrophosphate groups co-ordinated around the manganese, does not.

From the theoretical standpoint the best example of an oxidation-reduction process involving hydride transfer is the *Meerwein–Pondorff–Oppenauer reaction* whereby alcohols may be oxidized by ketones, or the reverse, by the use of aluminium alkoxides. Pondorff, in 1925, developing earlier work, showed that aluminium isopropoxide in refluxing dry isopropanol was an excellent specific reducing agent for the $C=O$ groups of aldehydes and ketones since other sensitive groups, e.g. $C=C$ and NO_2, were not affected. Conversely, Oppenauer, in 1937, showed that an equivalent of aluminium tert. butoxide in boiling acetone would smoothly oxidize primary and secondary alcohols. In each mixture the aluminium atom of the alkoxide co-ordinates with the oxygen atom of the ketone to give a complex which is spatially arranged so that the 'hydride anion' has little distance to move in the ensuing equilibrium mixture.

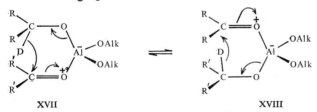

XVII	XVIII

In Pondorff's reaction, reduction is effected by distilling out the volatile ketonic component (acetone) and in Oppenauer's oxidation slow distillation of acetone, which is present in excess, takes with it isopropanol which is gradually produced by the oxidation of the original less volatile alcohol.

The intramolecular nature of the hydride shift has been shown by reducing cyclohexanone with $Me_2CD.OH$, when the resulting cyclohexanol was found to be deuterated. Conversely, an alcohol of the type R—O—D did not transfer its deuterium atom to form a C—D bond (*J.A.C.S.* 1952, **74**, 2404).

The Meerwein–Pondorff–Oppenauer reaction is losing its preparative value since sodium borohydride is now a cheaper, simpler and equally specific reducing agent, whilst for corresponding specific oxidations a suspension of active manganese dioxide in petroleum or carbon tetrachloride can often be used. This reagent for instance oxidizes allylic alcohols quite smoothly

$$R—CH{=}CH—CH_2—OH \longrightarrow R—CH{=}CH—CH{=}O$$

but as yet nothing definite can be said about the mechanism of such heterogeneous oxidation processes as this.

However, the equilibrium (XVII) $\rightleftharpoons$ (XVIII) is of theoretical importance, for it is a close model for the reversible enzymic oxidations,

$$>\!CH(OH) \rightleftharpoons\; >\!C{=}O + 2H\cdot$$

of alcohols, α-hydroxy-acids, carbohydrates, etc., which are effected by Warburg's co-enzymes I or II (DPN, TPN), both of which contain a nicotinamide group linked through the nitrogen atom of the pyridine ring to ribose and thence to a nucleotide. Vennesland and Westheimer have shown that deuterated ethanol, even in water, gives up its deuterium atom, reversibly, to the nicotinamide in the enzymic oxidation, and that the deuterated reduced co-enzyme (XX) can be used specifically to deuterate pyruvic acid to $Me.CD(OH).CO_2H$.

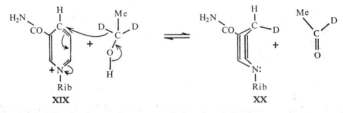

However, if 1-deutero-glucose and glucose dehydrogenase are used to reduce co-enzyme-I then the resulting deuterated reduced co-enzyme can transfer hydrogen, but not deuterium to pyruvic acid. Evidently in the reduced compound (XX) the C—H and C—D bonds are not stereochemically equivalent, and the activating enzyme must control the direction of approach of the alcohol or ketone to the nicotinamide group.

Westheimer has shown that N-benzylnicotinamide can reduce thiobenzophenone in the absence of an enzyme catalyst. The C=C bond of $\alpha\beta$-unsaturated ketones, e.g. $Ph . CO . CH{=}CH . CF_3$, can also be reduced by hydride transfer from a dihydropyridine derivative without the use of an enzyme catalyst (*J.A.C.S.* 1962, **84**, 792).

In living matter the Warburg co-enzymes act essentially as oxidants of simple alcoholic metabolites, for their reduced forms (XX) are promptly re-oxidized by another enzyme system (FAD); again, in model systems, this oxidation can be effected in the absence of any enzyme.

It is interesting to note that both in these enzyme reactions and those indicated on p. 66, electromeric changes within a pyridine ring facilitate the electron movement that with the C=O group can only be achieved by a strong acid catalyst or by co-ordination with a metal such as aluminium. The high polarizability of the pyridine, and similar, heterocyclic ring systems must evidently be one explanation of why these very complex molecules play such an important part in biological reactions.

General reading references (*additional to previous chapters*)

BELL, R. P., *The Proton in Chemistry*, Cornell University Press, 1959; Methuen, London, 1960.

GOULD, E. S., *Mechanism and Structure in Organic Chemistry*, Holt, Rinehart & Winston, New York, 1959.

MELANDER, L., *Isotope Effects on Reaction Rates*, Ronald Press Co., New York, 1960.

WATERS, W. A., *Chem. Soc. Quart. Reviews*, 1958, **12**, 277 (Oxidations by compounds of Chromium and Manganese).

CHAPTER 5

The Oxidation of 1,2-Glycols

The discovery in the 1930's of two complimentary oxidants which can cleave quantitatively the C—C bonds of 1,2-glycols has been of outstanding value in the elucidation of the structures of organic compounds of all types. The first of these, *lead tetra-acetate* should be used under anhydrous conditions in glacial acetic acid or benzene solution, but it must be remembered that in hot solution it is also a powerful general oxidant for several other organic groups; the second, *periodic acid*, is used in buffered aqueous solutions and so is particularly useful for the degradation of carbohydrates and water-soluble compounds of biological importance. These two reagents can break the C—C bonds of even primary and secondary glycols, e.g. $HO.CH_2—CH_2.OH$, but more recently it has been found that all the oxidants of monohydric alcohols can effect C—C cleavage of di-tertiary alcohols such as pinacol, though they tend preferably to oxidize primary and secondary 1,2-glycols by C—H bond fission. The following sections show how slight are the structural and electronic differences which lead to this discrimination in regard to the modes of oxidative action.

Lead tetra-acetate, obtained by heating red lead in glacial acetic acid containing some acetic anhydride,

1. $Pb_3O_4 + 8HO.CO.CH_3$
$$\longrightarrow Pb(O.CO.CH_3)_4 + 2Pb(O.CO.CH_3)_2 + 4H_2O$$

is immediately decomposed by water,

2. $Pb(O.CO.CH_3)_4 + 2H_2O \longrightarrow PbO_2 + 4HO.CO.CH_3$

and, in hot solution decomposes to give both acetate and methyl free radicals, though perhaps this decomposition first yields acetyl peroxide.

3. $Pb(O.CO.CH_3)_4 \longrightarrow Pb(O.CO.CH_3)_2 + 2.O.CO.CH_3$
$$\longrightarrow 2CO_2 + 2.CH_3$$

Consequently it can, like an acyl peroxide, be used as a homolytic oxidant and in boiling acetic acid exhibits all the reactions of $.CH_3$ and $.O.CO.CH_3$ radicals that have been reviewed in Chapter 3. Some of its high-temperature oxidations, e.g. of phenols, are undoubtedly heterolytic, resembling the acid-catalysed reactions of diacyl peroxides and so the thermal decomposition in a solvent such as acetic acid may perhaps be represented as passing through a hetero-lysis in which an acetate cation, $(CH_3.CO.O)^+$, is not liberated as such but combines at once with an electrophilic group.

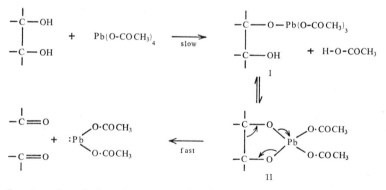

However, lead tetra-acetate does catalyse the thermal homolytic decomposition of alkyl hydroperoxides and also the autoxidation of hydrocarbons: evidently its mode of decomposition, (3) or (4), depends upon its environment.

Lead tetra-benzoate has been used as a source of phenyl radicals and phenyliodoso-acetate, $Ph—I(O.CO.CH_3)_2$, has been shown to behave exactly in the same manner. The latter too is a glycol splitting reagent.

Between 1931 and 1940, R. Criegee and his colleagues found that *cold* solutions of lead tetra-acetate reacted with all types of 1,2-glycols by a quantitative bimolecular reaction, which they represented as a cyclic heterolytic process,

for they found that the *cis*-glycols of 5- and 6-membered alicyclic rings were oxidized very much more easily than their *trans*-isomers. An alternative mechanism involving homolytic rupture of a glycol by the attack of $CH_3.CO.O\cdot$ radicals can be rejected since this would not have the degree of specificity needed: *free* $\cdot CH_3$ would certainly attack the C—H of a secondary glycol.

6

However, cyclic *trans*-glycols, including even *trans*-decalin-9,10-diol (III) can be attacked, though slowly, and fig. 1 shows how the rate of glycol fission can be correlated with ring size. No one has, as yet, isolated an intermediate cyclic lead compound of structure (II), though substances of type (I), e.g. CH_3—O—$Pb(O.COCH_3)_3$, have been prepared. Kinetic work has now established that lead tetra-acetate oxidation of glycols can (but need not necessarily) be an acid-base-catalysed elimination reaction of the first Criegee intermediate (I), e.g.

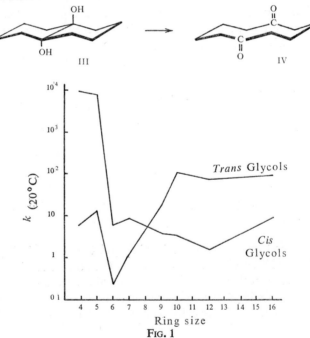

and this is the probable route of *trans*-glycol oxidation. The oxidation (III)→(IV) for instance is best effected in the presence of trichloro-acetic acid.

FIG. 1

Lead tetra-acetate can also be used for the fission of primary and secondary, but not tertiary amino-alcohols, and also for the oxidation of both α-hydroxy and α-keto-acids.

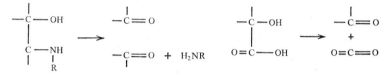

The last of these reactions may simulate the biochemical action of pyruvic acid as an acetylating agent for alcohols.

Periodic acid, H_5IO_6, and its salt, $NaIO_4$, sodium *meta*periodate, can be used in aqueous solution, either in the presence of mineral acid or in buffers down to pH 7. Alcohols and dioxane can be used as co-solvents. Like lead tetra-acetate it attacks cyclic *cis*- and *trans*-glycols at different rates and Bunton and his colleagues (*J. Chem. Soc.* 1957) have published both kinetic and spectroscopic evidence for the existence of the cyclic intermediate (V) which then decomposes slowly.

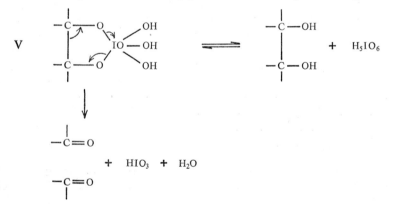

With *cis*- and *trans*-cyclohexane-1,2-diol the equilibrium constant for the cyclic complex formation is greater for the *trans* than for the *cis* diol, though the latter complex breaks much more quickly (*J. Chem. Soc.* 1959, 743).

Triols and poly-ols produce formic acid when oxidized, and if neutral $NaIO_4$ is used this can be estimated quantitatively by titration with alkali or, in a Warburg apparatus, by the liberation of an equivalent of CO_2 from a bicarbonate buffer.

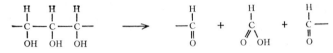

The consumption of periodate itself is best estimated in neutral solution by arsenite titration.

5. $$HIO_4 + Na_2HAsO_3 = HIO_3 + Na_2HAsO_4$$

These quantitative oxidations are most valuable for the elucidation of the structures of carbohydrates. Thus glucose and fructose oxidize differently:

6. $HO.CH_2.(CHOH)_4.CHO + 5HIO_4 = CH_2O + 5H.CO_2H + 5HIO_3$

7. $HO.CH_2.(CHOH)_3.CO.CH_2.OH + 4HIO_4$
$$= CH_2O + 3HCO_2H + HO_2C.CH_2.OH$$

8. then $HO_2C.CH_2.OH + HIO_4 = CO_2 + CH_2O$ (*very slow*)

The different yields of formic acid are diagnostic. The last stage of fructose oxidation is very slow because α-hydroxy-acids are very much more resistant to periodic acid than to lead tetra-acetate. From periodic acid the cyclic intermediate in the oxidation would be an acid anhydride and this would not easily form in water.

Whilst the pyranose rings of reducing sugars are hemi-acetals, and in water exist in equilibrium with hydrated acyclic molecules, so that glucose reacts as if it were $HO.CH_2.(CHOH)_4.CH(OH)_2$, all glycosides, being acetals, do not hydrolyse in neutral solution and so are attacked by periodic acid without fission of the ether link. The oxidation of α-methyl-D-glucoside has been used to show that it contains a 6-membered ring, and periodic acid oxidation was used to prove that the simple nucleotides contain a ribose unit with a furanose ring.

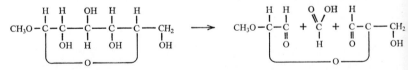

When periodic acid oxidation is applied to polysaccharides the percentage yields of formic acid and of formaldehyde, taken in relation

to the number of equivalents of periodic acid that are consumed, can often be diagnostic in structure elucidation.

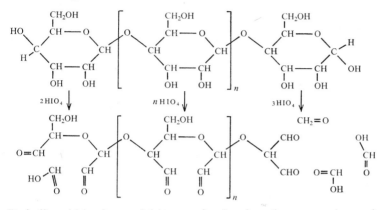

Periodic acid is also useful in protein chemistry because serine and threonine liberate ammonia quantitatively and so can be estimated in protein hydrolysates.

$$CH_2(OH)—CH(NH_2)—CO_2H \longrightarrow CH_2(=O) + O=CH—CO_2H + NH_3$$

Biochemists have developed several microchemical methods for the analysis of these simple products of periodate oxidations. These are particularly valuable when used in conjunction with chromatographic techniques for the separation of natural polymers and for the degradation of substances which have been synthesized *in vivo* from ^{14}C-labelled compounds. The course of photosynthesis of carbohydrates has been elucidated in this way. Again periodic acid can be used for investigating the microscopic structure of cellular tissue. For example, with thin slices of wood the cellulose can be destroyed whilst the lignin remains positionally intact.

Other examples of glycol fission

It has been found that any oxidant of a primary or secondary monohydric alcohol will also oxidize pinacol, $HO—CMe_2—CMe_2—OH$, to acetone, but usually oxidizes ethylene glycol to glyoxal and often oxidizes secondary alcohols concurrently by C—H and C—C fission. Evidently the concerted 1,4-elimination process needed for glycol fission occurs less easily than 1,2-elimination from a CH(OH) group unless it is stereochemically favoured by the formation of a cyclic intermediate such as (II) or (V).

In the case of chromic acid oxidation, di-tertiary 1,2-glycols are fairly easily oxidized in solutions of low acidity which have no effect on tert.butanol, but with primary and secondary glycols, e.g. $HO.CH_2.CH_2.OH$, the activation energy for C—H bond fission is the more favourable by 10 to 15 kilocalories. However, under similar conditions, *cis*-1,2-dimethylcyclopentan-1,2-diol oxidizes 1700 times as fast as its *trans* isomer and 47 times as fast as does pinacol in aqueous chromic acid (Rocek and Westheimer, *J.A.C.S.* 1962, 84, 2241). This difference in reaction velocities provides the best evidence as yet available for the formation of a cyclic intermediate compound. In the low acidity range the oxidation of pinacol is of first order with respect to the acid concentration, so that the transition complex could be either (VI) or (VII) and even pinacol monomethyl ether can be oxidized very slowly. It should be remembered that, on account of steric interactions, the staggered *trans* conformation of pinacol, in which the hydroxyl groups are widely separated, is more stable than the *cis* conformation from which a cyclic ester could be formed. So, as in the case of periodic acid oxidation of glycols, the rate of formation of the chromate ester is an important criterion in determining the ease of glycol fission.

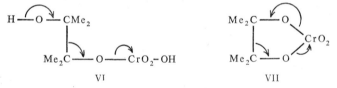

VI   VII

Slack and Waters (*J. Chem. Soc.* 1949, 594) isolated from carbon tetrachloride solution an intermediate adduct of pinacol with two molecules of chromyl chloride and considered that this might break homolytically to Cr^V, but an acyclic heterolytic elimination is quite as probable.

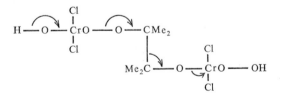

However, the formation of cyclic complexes is definitely involved in the oxidation of pinacol by quinquevalent vanadium for this oxidation, which is of first order with respect both to pinacol and vanadium-(V), is acid catalysed at a rate given by the expression

$$-d[V^V]/dt = k.[Pinacol].[Vanadium-(V)].(1 + a.h_0)$$

where h_0 is the Hammett acidity function, indicative of *proton*, (H⁺), catalysis. Since part of the oxidation is not an acid-catalysed reaction this must be effected by the ion VO_2^+, and since the acid-catalysed reaction involves only an extra proton the two reaction complexes must be (VIII) and (IX)

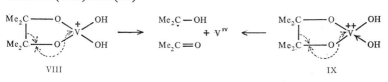

In contrast, pinacol monomethyl ether oxidizes slowly by an acid catalysed reaction which, like that of a monohydric alcohol (p. 56) has a rate dependent upon acid *concentration*, so that the oxidant ion in this case must be $\{V(OH)_3\}^{2+}$, i.e. (X) (Jones, Littler and Waters, *J. Chem. Soc.* 1961, 630).

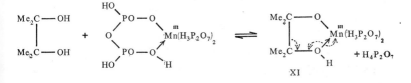

The one-electron oxidant manganic pyrophosphate also attacks pinacol, but the rate, whilst of first order with respect to Mn^{III}, is not of first order with respect to pinacol, though 1/(oxidation rate) varies as 1/[Pinacol]. This type of reaction kinetics indicates that the reaction involves an initial reversible displacement of a pyrophosphate ligand group by a pinacol molecule and that only the co-ordinated pinacol (XI), which must be formed to a considerable extent, is oxidized.

Some oxidations of 1,2-glycols by ceric salts show similar kinetics.

There is definite evidence that these transition metal ions split the pinacol molecule to give one molecule of acetone and one isopropanol radical, $Me_2\overset{\centerdot}{C}$—OH, for if acrylonitrile is added to the oxidizing mixtures then a polymer containing hydroxylated end-groups is precipitated from solution, thus:

9. $Me_2C(OH)\cdot + CH_2{=}CH{-}CN \longrightarrow Me_2C(OH){-}CH_2{-}CH(CN)\cdot$

and if the oxidation is carried out in the presence of mercuric chloride then the intermediate organic radical reduces some of the mercuric chloride to insoluble mercurous chloride,

10. $Me_2\overset{\centerdot}{C}{-}OH + Hg^{2+} \longrightarrow Me_2C{=}O + Hg^+ + H^+$

Again, it has been shown (*J.A.C.S.* 1959, **81**, 1494) that in the oxidation of pinacol by ceric sulphate one molecule of acetone is produced per Ce^{IV} ion, but when acrylamide, which then polymerizes, is added, only one molecule of acetone is produced for every two molecules of Ce^{IV}, since the radical $Me_2\overset{\centerdot}{C}$—OH then produces polymer radical

$$Me_2C(OH){-}(CH_2{-}CH.CONH_2)_n{-}CH_2{-}CH(CONH_2)\cdot$$

which eventually reduces the second ceric ion

11. $H_2O + {-}CH_2{-}CH(CONH_2)\cdot + Ce^{4+} + H_2O$
$$\longrightarrow {-}CH_2{-}CH(CONH_2){-}OH + Ce^{3+} + H^+$$

Attempts have been made to use this type of oxidation with cellulose for the production of graft polymers.

Just as lead tetra-acetate will oxidize α-hydroxy-acids to carbon dioxide and an aldehyde or ketone, so the ions of V^V, Ce^{IV} and Mn^{III} degrade α-hydroxy-acids to carbon dioxide and organic radicals. Again, the hydrogen ion dependence with vanadium-(V) shows that two cyclic complexes, (XII) and (XIII), can be involved.

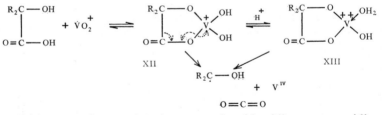

With manganic pyrophosphate, tartaric acid oxidizes more rapidly as a 1,2-glycol than as an α-hydroxy-acid and, as would be expected

from cyclic complexes of different configuration, racemic and meso-
tartaric acids oxidize at different rates (*J. Chem. Soc.* 1955, 217).

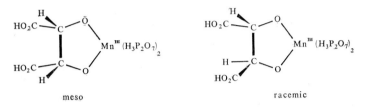

meso   racemic

Excellent examples of homolytic glycol fission are afforded by the
thermal decompositions of both ethylene glycol dinitrite and of ethylene glycol dinitrate.

$$CH_2 \!-\! O \!-\! NO_2 \qquad\qquad CH_2 \!=\! O \qquad NO_2$$
$$\qquad\qquad\qquad\qquad\qquad\qquad + $$
$$CH_2 \!-\! O \!-\! NO_2 \qquad\qquad CH_2 \!=\! O \qquad NO_2$$

Similarly, 1,4-butane-diol dinitrite splits to give formaldehyde and
ethylene, whilst 1,3-propane-diol dinitrite decomposes as follows
(L. P. Kuhn, *J.A.C.S.* 1956, **78**, 2719):

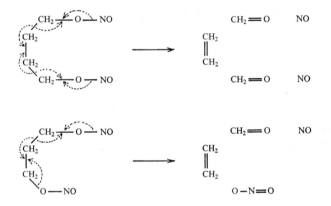

These pyrolyses probably occur in consecutive stages and do not
involve ring formation.

For general reading references, *see Chapter IV*

CHAPTER 6

Oxidations of Aldehydes

Heterolytic oxidations

Aldehydes can be oxidized, in ionizing solvents, by all the heterolytic reagents which attack alcohols and often their reactions are so much more rapid that, by the gradual addition of the oxidizer, it is possible to effect selective oxidation of, say, the aldehydic group of a reducing sugar. The oxidations of aldehydes by chromic acid and by permanganate have indeed been shown to involve concerted eliminations of the type discussed in Chapter 4.

Thus the *permanganate* oxidation of benzaldehyde has been shown by Wiberg and Stewart (*J.A.C.S.* 1956, **78**, 1214) to be an acid catalysed reaction in which the permanganate anion adds, through oxygen, to the carbon centre of the carbonium ion, Ph—$\overset{+}{\text{C}}$H—OH, and the C—H group of the aldehyde is broken in the following, rate-determining, step since Ph—CDO oxidizes at $\frac{1}{7}$ of the rate of Ph—CHO.

$$\text{Ph}-\text{CH}=\text{O} + \text{H}^+ \rightleftharpoons \text{Ph}-\overset{+}{\text{C}}\text{H}-\text{OH} \rightleftharpoons \underset{\overset{18*}{\text{O}}-\text{MnO}_3}{\text{Ph}-\text{C}-\text{H}} \overset{\text{slow}}{\longrightarrow} \underset{\overset{18*}{\text{O}}}{\text{Ph}-\text{C}} + \underset{\text{MnO}_3}{\text{H}}$$

Substituted benzaldehydes with electron-withdrawing groups, e.g. NO_2—C_6H_4—CHO, oxidize more slowly than benzaldehyde itself. This is to be expected since the substituent would reduce the ease of proton addition to the C=O group and so diminish the equilibrium constant of the first, rapid, reaction stage.

In the hands of these investigators, the ^{18}O-labelling of the permanganate ion has been diagnostic in the elucidation of the mechanisms of many oxidation processes. In the above instance it is known that the $(\text{Mn}^{18}\text{O}_4)^-$ ion does not exchange its oxygen atom with water, and that benzoic acid, Ph—$\text{C}^{18}\text{O}_2\text{H}$, exchanges oxygen very slowly indeed.

To prepare the $(\text{Mn}^{18}\text{O}_4)^-$ anion, permanganate is first warmed, in H_2^{18}O, with very strong alkali, when the permanganate is slowly reduced to manganate, with evolution of oxygen from the water molecules (M. C. R. Symons, *J. Chem. Soc.* 1954, 3676),

1. $\qquad 4(MnO_4)^- + 4(OH)^- \longrightarrow 4(MnO_4)^{2-} + 2H_2O + O_2$

a reaction which may proceed through the equilibrium

2. $\qquad (MnO_4)^- + (OH)^- \rightleftharpoons (MnO_4)^{2-} + \cdot OH$

and oxidation of hydroxyl radicals through hydrogen peroxide. Unlike the *per*manganate anion, the manganate anion, $(MnO_4)^{2-}$, can exchange its oxygen with water, probably because the second dissociation constant of manganic acid is low enough for the formation of the anion $(HMnO_4)^-$ which could be expected to undergo nucleophilic displacement at the manganese atom by another hydroxyl group:

3. $\qquad (H^{18}O)^- + (O_3Mn{-}OH)^- \rightleftharpoons (H^{18}O{-}MnO_3)^- + (OH)^-$

On acidification, manganates rapidly disproportionate to permanganate, with deposition of manganese dioxide.

4. $\qquad 3(MnO_4)^{2-} + 4H^+ \longrightarrow 2(MnO_4)^- + MnO_2 + 2H_2O$

The oxygen transfer to benzaldehyde, which also occurs in the permanganate oxidation of olefins (Chapter 8), gives clear evidence for the formation, in acid solutions, of the unstable manganite anion $(MnO_3)^-$, a derivative of Mn^V, but the subsequent reactions of this ion are as yet quite unknown.

The foregoing mechanism for the acid-catalysed oxidation of aldehydes is not applicable to alkaline permanganate oxidation under circumstances in which the manganate ion represents the stable valency level of manganese. Alkali only slightly accelerates the rate of oxidation of benzaldehyde and it is possible that this oxidation may be homolytic in type. However, these conditions are not, in general, appropriate for effecting aldehyde oxidations, since aliphatic aldehydes would then aldolize and aromatic aldehydes undergo the Cannizzaro reaction.

The slower oxidation of benzaldehyde by *chromic acid* shows similar kinetic features both in water and in acetic acid (*J.A.C.S.* 1958, **80**, 3022, 3030), but has a slightly lower kinetic isotope effect (k_H/k_D, 4·3) and electron-attracting substituents reduce the reaction rate. Consequently it too can be represented as occurring by a concerted elimination although this cannot be verified by the use of ^{18}O.

$$Ph-CH=O \;+\; H_2CrO_4 \;\rightleftharpoons\; Ph-\overset{\displaystyle OH}{\underset{\displaystyle O-CrO_3H}{\underset{|}{\overset{|}{C}}}}\!\!-H \;\xrightarrow{slow}\; Ph-\overset{\displaystyle OH}{\underset{\displaystyle O}{\overset{|}{\underset{\|}{C}}}} +(H_2CrO_3)$$

If this oxidation is carried out in the presence of air then some oxygen is absorbed and the rate of consumption of the chromic acid also increases. This shows that one, at least, of the intermediate valency levels of chromium must also attack the benzaldehyde directly and produce traces of free benzoyl radicals, Ph—CO·, which are evidently oxidized directly by chromic acid.

It is interesting to note that, in the permanganate oxidation of benzaldehyde, the $(MnO_4)^-$ anion can add to an electrophilic carbon atom so that thereafter the C—H bond can be broken by proton loss. In alcohol oxidation by permanganate (p. 68), since no addition of the $(MnO_4)^-$ ion is possible, hydride transfer occurs and there is no ^{18}O exchange with the organic molecule. Hydride transfers appear to require more activation energy than proton eliminations, for the permanganate oxidation of aldehydes is much more facile than the permanganate oxidation of alcohols: with chromic acid, where a similar mechanism is operative in both cases, alcohols and aldehydes oxidize at comparable speeds and it is often possible to effect the partial oxidation, $R—CH_2—OH \rightarrow R—CH=O$. The safest way of checking further oxidation is to work in acetic anhydride solution, when the aldehyde is stabilized as $R—CH(O.COCH_3)_2$.

In respect to both chromic acid and permanganate, formic acid behaves as a typical aldehyde. Its permanganate oxidation is, however, base-catalysed and so is a reaction of the anion: it shows $k_H/k_D = 7\cdot4$ and ^{18}O transfer to the resulting carbon dioxide occurs.

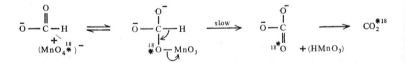

Oxidations of aldehydes by bromine-water, or by hypobromite, can be represented similarly, but in practice these reactions are not particularly to be recommended for aliphatic aldehydes since, especially in acid solution, concurrent bromine substitution involving enolization may also occur.

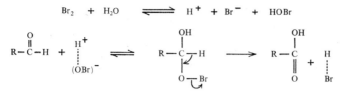

Still another example of the oxidative elimination reaction of aldehydes is afforded by the dehydration of an aldoxime by acetic anhydride, which is often the most suitable route for selective reaction in a molecule that contains other oxidizable groups.

$$R-CH=O \; + \; H_2N-OH \longrightarrow R-C \overset{H}{\underset{\underset{OH}{|}}{\Vert}} N \xrightarrow{Ac_2O} R-C\equiv N \xrightarrow{H^+} R-CO_2H \\ + \\ NH_3$$

Whilst the above reactions involve oxidation by proton loss, the *Cannizzaro reaction* can be cited as a good example of oxidation by hydride transfer (mechanism B of p. 58). It can be effected by treating aromatic aldehydes by strong alkali and its mechanism has been established by the use of deuterated aldehydes. As the following diagram shows, the reaction process is similar to that of the Meerwein–Pondorff–Oppenauer reaction. The *crossed Cannizzaro reaction*, in which formaldehyde is employed as the reducing agent, is of considerable preparative value.

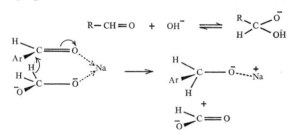

Aliphatic aldehydes, other than Me_3C—CHO, aldolize with much weaker alkali than that required for effecting the Cannizzaro reaction, but the important synthesis of penterythritol, which is best effected by using lime-water, clearly has a Cannizzaro reaction as its final step:

$$CH_3-CHO + 3CH_2O \longrightarrow (HO-CH_2)_3C-CHO$$
$$(HO-CH_2)_3C-CHO + CH_2O \longrightarrow (HO-CH_2)_4C + H-CO_2H$$

α-Keto-aldehydes easily undergo an intermolecular Cannizzaro reaction with dilute alkali:

$$R—CO—CHO \longrightarrow R—CH(OH)—CO_2H$$

and so α-hydroxy acids often result from the hydrolysis of halogenated ketones, e.g.

$$Ph—CO—CH_3 \longrightarrow Ph—CO—CHCl_2 \longrightarrow Ph—CH(OH)—CO_2H$$

Homolytic oxidations

Both aliphatic and aromatic aldehydes are easily autoxidized (Chapter 2) and the initial product is a per-acid which, however, can react with more aldehyde by an acid-catalysed heterolytic reaction of the type described above.

This heterolysis is favoured by the presence of water and since homolysis of the per-acid

5. $$R.CO.O—OH \longrightarrow R.CO.O\cdot + \cdot OH$$

auto-catalyses the autoxidation chain (p. 12), moisture somewhat retards aldehyde autoxidation. Both neutral conditions and autoxidation in acetic anhydride, which stabilizes the per-acid as the mixed anhydride $R.CO.O—O.CO.CH_3$, favour oxygen uptake.

At temperatures of over 100° the autoxidation of aliphatic aldehydes can be complicated by the production of carbon monoxide by the chain reactions

6. $$R.CO\cdot \longrightarrow R\cdot + CO$$
7. $$R\cdot + R.CHO \longrightarrow R.H + R.CO\cdot$$

which are important in the combustion of organic compounds in a limited supply of air. This decomposition can be promoted by the addition of thiols which act as chain-transfer agents

8. $$R\cdot + H—S—R' \longrightarrow R—H + \cdot S—R'$$
9. $$R'—S\cdot + R—CHO \longrightarrow R'—S—H + R—CO\cdot$$

Aromatic radicals, e.g. $Ph—CO\cdot$, are too much resonance-stabilized to lose carbon monoxide at this moderate temperature. Many other free radicals, e.g. alkyloxy, $R—O\cdot$, can dehydrogenate aldehydes by reaction (7) above, but are of little practical use, except as catalysts of autoxidation, since they do not effect the ultimate conversion of an aldehyde to a carboxylic acid.

In aqueous solution aliphatic aldehydes are easily oxidized by a whole group of one-electron-abstracting reagents, such as Cu^{II} (Fehling's and Benedict's solutions), $\{Ag(NH_3)_2\}^+$, $\{Fe(CN)_6\}^{3-}$, complexed ions of Mn^{III}, Ce^{IV}. and V^V, and the inorganic radical $\cdot ON(SO_3K)_2$, under mild conditions in which neither alcohols nor olefins are attacked. Though some of these reagents are qualitatively important for the detection of the —CHO group, none of them, with the possible exception of $Ag(NH_3)_2^+$, of which the mechanism of action is quite unknown, are of preparative use for the conversion of an aldehyde to the corresponding carboxylic acid and in general they have little action on formaldehyde, benzaldehyde or chloral hydrate. Several equivalents of such oxidants can be consumed per molecule of aldehyde and, if used in excess, the end-product appears to be formic acid from a n-aldehyde and a ketone from a branched-chain aldehyde.

Kinetic studies have shown that these oxidations are acid or base-catalysed, and the alkaline oxidations are complicated by aldolization. With the fairly active oxidant manganic pyrophosphate it was found by Drummond and Waters that the oxidations of simple aliphatic aldehydes were zero order reactions with respect to the oxidant, and for the easily oxidized isobutyraldehyde, $Me_2CH.CHO$, this has also been shown to be the case for two other oxidants, though the less reactive aldehydes often oxidize by first-order processes with respect to the oxidant. Now zero-order reactions of any carbonyl compound are indicative of a process dependent upon a rate-controlling enolization and so these aldehyde oxidations can all be represented by the sequence

10. $R_2CH-CH{=}O + H^+ \rightleftharpoons R_2CH-\overset{+}{C}H-OH$ (*immediate*)

11. $R_2CH-\overset{+}{C}H-OH + {:}B \rightleftharpoons R_2C{=}CH-OH + (HB)^+$ (*slow*)

12. $R_2C{=}CH-OH \rightleftharpoons R_2C{=}CH-O^- + H^+$ (*immediate*)

13. $R_2C{=}CH-O^- \xrightarrow{-e} R_2C{=}CH-O\cdot \longleftrightarrow \overset{\cdot}{R_2}C-CH{=}O$

which should yield a mesomeric radical. Thus the oxidative step (13) should be facile and, if it is faster than the forward step (11), the whole reaction will become of zero order with respect to the oxidant. Further oxidation of the mesomeric radical, $R_2C{=}CH{-}O \cdot \leftrightarrow R_2\overset{\cdot}{C}{-}CH{=}O$, would, of course, give the carbonium ion $R_2\overset{+}{C}{-}CH{=}O$, and thence the α-hydroxy-aldehyde $R_2C(OH){-}CH{=}O$. This has in fact been shown, for more than one oxidant, to be the first product of the oxidation of isobutyraldehyde. For example, oxidation of this aldehyde with the radical $(KSO_3)_2NO \cdot$ gave methyl acraldehyde, $CH_2{=}CMe{-}CHO$, whilst oxidation with hot alkaline ferricyanide gave the dihydropyrazine derivative (I).

Usually these initial oxidation products are oxidized more easily than the initial aldehydes. The later stages in aldehyde oxidation may well follow a similar route involving successive enolizations of $-\overset{|}{C}H{-}CO{-}$ groups, for it has been shown that the oxidations of glucose and of acetoin and benzoin by cupric complexes proceed by transformation to the ene-diol, which again can yield a resonance-stabilized radical.

Though these oxidations are of zero order with respect to Cu^{II} they appear to be slower than the preceding enolizations. The kinetic features here may, however, depend upon the stabilities of chelated cuprous and cupric complexes and are not fully understood. However, the ease of oxidation of an acyloin via its ene-diol serves to explain why both aldose and ketose sugars are almost as easily oxidized as an aliphatic aldehyde.

A few special cases of aldehyde oxidation merit comment. Acraldehyde, $CH_2{=}CH{-}CH{=}O$, and crotonaldehyde, $Me{-}CH{-}CH{=}CH{=}O$, which cannot form enols of normal type are quite easily oxidized in acid solution, but react by first forming mesomeric actions and then the enol of a β-hydroxy-aldehyde

$CH_2{=}CH{-}CH{=}O + H^+$

$$\rightleftharpoons CH_2{=}CH{-}\overset{+}{C}H{-}OH \longleftrightarrow \overset{+}{C}H_2{-}CH{=}CH{-}OH$$

$\overset{+}{C}H_2{-}CH{=}CH{-}OH + H_2O \longrightarrow HO{-}CH_2{-}CH{=}CH{-}OH$

which can oxidize normally.

Tertiary valeraldehyde, Me_3C—CHO, which cannot enolize, has proved to be, like benzaldehyde, inert to attack by Fehling's solution, whilst again, chloral hydrate is first hydrolysed to chloroform and formate before the latter is oxidized in alkaline media.

Formaldehyde, however, can be oxidized slowly, but kinetic studies have shown that its reactions are typically those of an alcohol, i.e. $CH_2(OH)_2$, and indeed it is almost completely hydrated in aqueous solution. With all reagents as yet examined the isotopic molecule $CD_2(OH)_2$ oxidizes more slowly than does $CH_2(OH)_2$.

General reading reference

WATERS, W. A., 'Homolytic Oxidation Processes', In *Progress in Organic Chemistry*, Vol. 5. Butterworths, London, 1961.

(*See also the general references to chapters II and IV.*)

7

CHAPTER 7

Oxidations of Ketones, Related Compounds and Carboxylic Acids

Ketones are much less easy to oxidize than are aldehydes or olefins, but they can be specifically oxidized by several reagents which do not attack saturated hydrocarbons or even alcohols. Only the peroxides and the per-acids, which have been described in Chapter 3, oxidize ketones by direct attack on the carbonyl group and these reagents are distinctive in that they can oxidize, without difficulty, purely aromatic ketones, such as benzophenone, to which other strong oxidants such as chromic acid or permanganate are quite inert. Other reagents oxidize ketones by attacking C—H groups adjacent to the C=O, and both for heterolytic and for homolytic reactions a clear connection can be traced between the ease of oxidation and the ease of enolization of any ketone. Acetone, which is slow to enolize in acid solution, is decidedly more difficult to oxidize than its homologues and this fact has often given a false impression with regard to ketone stability.

All the heterolytic oxidations of ketones are influenced by acid or base catalysis and the reagents which easily attack the active C—H groups of ketones also react with the active C—H groups of other tautomeric systems, e.g. —CH—N=O, —CH—C=N—, and, to some extent, —CH=CH—CH₂—, as in aromatic side-chains. Consequently, oxidations of compounds such as nitroparaffins, heterocyclic bases such as α-picoline and allylic molecules can be included in this chapter.

Heterolytic oxidations of ketones
If, as suggested above, heterolytic oxidations of ketones and related molecules can be correlated with tautomeric change then the upper limit of the oxidation rate of any such substance should be that of the slow ionization of a C—H bond. Under basic conditions this is the forward reaction (1) below and under acid conditions reaction (3).

1. $-\overset{\underset{|}{H}}{\underset{|}{C}}-C{=}O + :B \rightleftharpoons -\overset{-}{\underset{|}{C}}-C{=}O + (HB)^+ \longleftrightarrow -\underset{|}{C}{=}\underset{|}{C}-O^-$

2. $-\underset{|}{CH}-C{=}O + HA \rightleftharpoons -\underset{|}{CH}-\overset{+}{\underset{|}{C}}-O-H + (:A)^-$

3. $-\overset{\underset{|}{H}}{\underset{|}{C}}-\overset{+}{\underset{|}{C}}-O-H + :B \rightleftharpoons -\underset{|}{C}{=}\underset{|}{C}-O-H + (HB)^+$

It is customary to measure rates of enolization of ketones by controlled bromination, for the rate of halogenation of an enol, or of its anion, is so much more rapid than the rate of enolization that the bromination is, except in extreme cases, a reaction of zero order with respect to the halogen. Actually the halogenation of a ketone should be regarded as an oxidation, but only in the case of methyl ketones, which in alkaline solution undergo the *haloform reaction*, e.g. (4)

4. $R.CO.CH_3 + 3Br_2 \longrightarrow R.CO.CBr_3 \xrightarrow{\ OH^-\ } R.CO.OH + HCBr_3$

are halogens of any practical value as ketone oxidants, for the electrophilic character of C=O, which facilitates the ionization of C—H, decreases the ease of hydrolysis of C—Br and, if forcing conditions (e.g. NaOEt in EtOH) are used, then a molecular rearrangement (Favorski reaction) may occur instead. Halogenation, however, provides the simplest route for the oxidation of the

$$N{=}\underset{|}{C}-\underset{|}{C}-H \quad \text{and} \quad -\underset{|}{C}{=}\underset{|}{C}-\underset{|}{C}-H$$

systems, as in α-picoline or toluene, but with such molecules this reaction is often carried out homolytically.

Substituent groups affect the acid- and base-catalysed enolizations of ketones in opposite ways. Thus the rate of the forward base-catalysed reaction (1) of a ketone R—CH$_2$—CO—R′ is increased by replacing hydrogen by a group R which attracts electrons and so facilitates the separation of proton from the CH$_2$ group, but the group R also attracts electrons away from the C=O group and so reduces the rate of the forward acid-catalysed reaction (2). For this reason it is not possible to check the base-catalysed halogenation of a methyl ketone, R—CO—CH$_3$ before complete halogenation to R—CO—Hal$_3$, but in acid solution the intermediates R—CO—CH$_2$—Hal and

R—CO—CH(Hal)$_2$ can both be isolated. Similarly, alkyl groups depress the rate of base-catalysed enolizations. However, the tautomeric equilibria reached in keto-enol and similar systems do not depend upon the nature of the catalyst but on the thermodynamic stabilities of the two tautomeric molecules, and of their common mesomeric ion. Hence an oxidation which involves a slow attack on an enol molecule may not follow the same course as one which depends on the rate of formation of an enol, for actually it is a general rule of tautomeric change that the tautomer which is most easily formed from, or converted to, the mesomeric ion is the one which is thermodynamically the least stable. Differences between the reactivities of selenium dioxide and of nitrous acid, for example, can be explained in this way.

In reviewing oxidation mechanisms, however, it is of value to consider why enols react with halogens so very much more rapidly than do simple olefins. Whereas bromine addition to $>$C=C$<$ involves the formation of a bromonium ion (I) of fairly high energy content the reaction with an enol can be a concerted process (II) which immediately gives stable products.

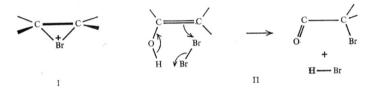

Since the bromine combines with the π-electrons of the enol the first product from a ketone such as cyclohexanone is thought to be the *axial* bromo derivative, but this rapidly isomerizes to the more stable equatorial isomer.

It is safe to conclude that other oxidations of ketones occur via enols if they are acid- or base-catalysed reactions which proceed at the enolization rate and are of zero order with respect to the oxidant (J. S. Littler, *J. Chem. Soc.* 1962, 827). This is the case for oxidation with acid *permanganate* and with both mercuric and thallic perchlorates, all of which also oxidize olefins easily. *Lead tetra-acetate* in acetic acid has again been reported to oxidize ketones by a zero-order reaction which can be represented as follows, and corresponds to the heterolytic reaction of lead tetra-acetate with glycols (p. 73).

Chromic acid, which slowly attacks olefins in strong acid solution (Chapter 8), also oxidizes ketones under similar conditions, but the oxidation occurs more slowly than does the enolization and isotope studies have been needed for the elucidation of its mechanism. With cyclohexanone the reaction velocity is proportional to the acidity of the solution and is of first order with respect to both the ketone and to the dominant chromate ion $(HCrO_4)^-$. Deuteration of the $-CH_2-CO-CH_2-$ group reduces the *initial* reaction rate, but this isotope effect may be ascribed to the slow step (reaction 3 of p. 91 of the enolization process, for the solvent isotope effect $(k_{D_2O}/k_{H_2O}=4-5)$ indicates that the oxidation involves *two* acid-base equilibria, one of which must be due to the dissociation

5. $$H_2CrO_4 \rightleftharpoons HCrO_4^- + H^+$$

whilst the other can be assigned to the fast equilibrium (reaction 2 of p. 91) involved in acid-catalysed enolization (see *J. Chem. Soc.* 1962, 822). The rate-determining stage in the ketone oxidation can therefore be written as a concerted addition to an enol, which at once gives a hypothetical Cr^{IV} ester of an α-hydroxy-ketone that could be expected to hydrolyse rapidly.

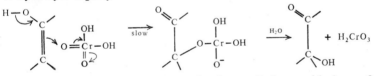

This concerted mechanism can also be applied to oxidations of *βγ*-unsaturated ketones which occur with double-bond shift

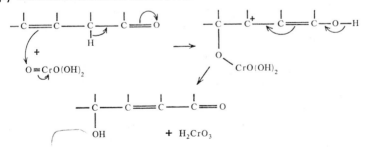

and is in full accord with available evidence concerning olefin oxidation.

In oxidations of ketones, chromic acid exhibits many features which characterize oxidations by *selenium dioxide*, which is a valuable reagent for the conversion of —CO—CH$_2$— to —CO—CO— and, unlike chromic acid, is not an oxidant of alcohols at moderate temperatures.

Oxidation with selenium dioxide is usually carried out in hot acetic acid in which selenic acid, H$_2$SeO$_3$, a weak acid ($K_1 = 2\cdot4 \times 10^{-3}$), is undissociated. The oxidation of desoxybenzoin has been studied kinetically by Corey and Schaefer (*J.A.C.S.* 1960, **82**, 918, see also *ibid.* 1962, **84**, 717) in 70% acetic acid and found to be of first order with respect to both selenium dioxide and to the desoxybenzoin. It is catalysed by mineral acids and also by moderate amounts of sodium acetate but the addition of enough of this to convert the selenic acid to the acid salt NaHSeO$_3$ completely stops the oxidation.

Since sodium acetate behaves as a base with respect to acetic acid these facts show that both acid-catalysed and base-catalysed oxidation of desoxybenzoin can occur and are indicative of a process related to enolization. Further support for this view comes from the fact that electron-supplying substituents (e.g. Me, MeO), when introduced into the benzoyl group of the Ph—CO—CH$_2$—Ph, accelerate the acid-catalysed reaction but retard the sodium-acetate-catalysed reaction, though similar substituents in the Ph—CH$_2$ group have smaller effects but of opposite sense. The acid-catalysed reaction had a large kinetic isotope effect ($k_H/k_D = 6$ at 89°) and so it is clear that complete keto $\rightleftharpoons$ enol equilibrium cannot proceed the rate-determining stage of the oxidation. As with the chromic acid oxidation, discussed above, the oxidation may, however, be written as a rapid concerted reaction of an enol so as to give a hypothetical Se^{II} ester of the ketone (III), which could then eliminate both elementary selenium and a water molecule so as to yield benzil and free selenium.

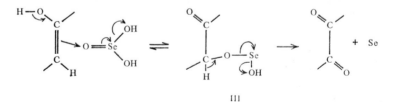

III

The oxidation of any other reactive methylene group may be represented similarly, e.g.

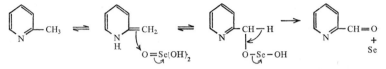

Many years ago Russian workers suggested that these oxidations involved decompositions of selenite esters (IV), but there is no reason to suppose that these could be formed rapidly from enols since it is difficult to esterify alcohols with selenious acid, and again these esters would have to rearrange to Se^{II} esters, (III) above, for the introduction of an oxygen atom into the reaction product. Corey and Schaefer suggested that the rate-determining process is the formation of the enol selenite ester (IV) from the carbonyl form of the ketone, but this is both unnecessary to account for the finding of an *initial* kinetic isotope effect and is a restricted mechanism that cannot be extended to oxidations of other active methylene groups, as in α-picoline which has been instanced above.

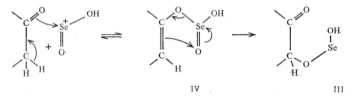

IV   III

The concerted mechanism can also be applied to the oxidation of 1,4-diketones, which is one of the few examples of a selenium dioxide oxidation that does not introduce an oxygen atom into the reaction product.

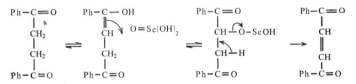

With complex steroids this oxidation has been studied kinetically by Banerji, Barton and Cookson (*J. Chem. Soc.* 1957, 5041), who have compared oxidation rates and bromination rates of 1,4-diketones and have shown that these run parallel for eight different compounds, though the oxidations are of first order with respect to selenium whilst the brominations are of zero order with respect to bromine. Again oxidation via enolization is indicated.

It would appear that in all these oxidations the breakdown of the selenium-(II) intermediate should be measurably slow and, moreover, the various reactions that lead to the formation of this unstable intermediate must all be reversible, for with ketones selenium dioxide is effective for converting —CH₂—CO to CO—CO—, but does not oxidize the single C—H of a $\overset{C}{\underset{C}{>}}$CH—CO— group though this can enolize easily.

Though ideally selenium dioxide oxidation of an organic compound should yield only the desired reaction product and insoluble selenium it often involves experimental difficulties because selenium may separate from the reaction mixture as a troublesome colloid.

Nitrous acid, alkyl nitrites and *organic nitroso-compounds* are another group of reagents which can be used to convert —CH₂—CO— to —CO—CO—. These act by forming condensation products easily split by acid hydrolysis.

$$\begin{array}{c} \diagdown \\ CO \\ | \\ CH_2 \diagup \end{array} + \; O{=}N{-}OH \longrightarrow \begin{array}{c} \diagdown \\ CO \\ | \\ C{=}N{-}OH \diagup \end{array} \xrightarrow{\text{H}^+} \begin{array}{c} \diagdown \\ CO \\ | \\ CO \diagup \end{array} + \; H_2NOH$$

Both acid-catalysed and base-catalysed processes may be used. With simple water-soluble ketones sodium nitrite and dilute mineral acid may conveniently be used for forming the iso-nitroso compound, but with higher ketones it is better to use an absolute alcohol solution of an alkyl nitrite together with sodium ethoxide as the condensing agent. An organic base, such as piperidine, is suitable for effecting condensations of organic nitroso-compounds with active methylene groups.

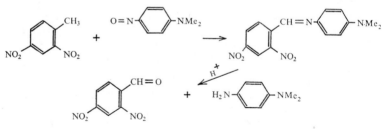

The first stage in the condensation of an alkyl nitrite with a ketone is a Claisen condensation with the mesomeric enol-anion of the ketone. This occurs preferably in the direction of most abundant enolization of the ketone which is not always the same as the direction of most rapid proton loss. Usually tertiary C—H is attacked preferably to —CH$_2$—. For instance, menthone (V) reacts as follows with ethyl nitrite and sodium ethoxide: the ring fission of the final stage is similar in mechanism to the alkaline cleavage of acetoacetic ester and it has had useful synthetic applications, as for instance in the Woodward and Doering synthesis of quinine.

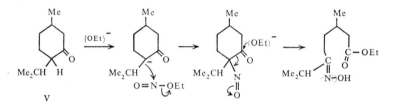

Homolytic oxidation of ketones

Active free radicals attack ketones at C—H bonds adjacent to the carbonyl group, because this yields a resonance-stabilized radical,

which by dimerizing can yield a 1,4-diketone. However, homolytic reactions between organic peroxides and ketones have seldom been put to practical use, except for the synthesis of α-branched ketones by addition of the above radicals to olefins.

Ketones again can be autoxidized fairly easily in the α-position to C=O, especially in strongly alkaline solution. This too is a homolytic chain reaction for it is sensitive to both peroxide and metal ion catalysis. However, autoxidations of ketones do not often give good yields of simple products, partly on account of the diversity of following ketone–peroxide reactions of types mentioned in Chapter 3, and partly due to the ease with which ketones and their immediate oxidation products undergo base-catalysed self condensations.

Acyloins (VI) which can result, with other products, from autoxidations of simple ketones have been shown to autoxidize via their enol anions (VII), for these very easily give stable radicals (VIII) of semi-quinone type (Weissberger, *J. Chem. Soc.* 1935, 223).

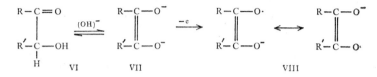

Radical-ions of this type are involved in oxidations of ascorbic acid and of reducing sugars. In buffered solutions such substances are easily attacked by oxygen if a trace of a copper or iron salt is present.

It has been found that all the ions of the transition metals which attack enolizable aliphatic aldehydes can also be used to oxidize ketones and nitroparaffins, though with these substances they act more slowly. For instance, potassium ferricyanide can be used to oxidize aldehydes in a bicarbonate buffer, but caustic soda is needed as the base catalyst for the oxidation of acetone at a similar rate. Since all these one-electron oxidations of ketones have been found to be acid- or base-catalysed it was thought, for some years, that enolization preceded oxidation, especially since the ultimate oxidation was always effected adjacent to the carbonyl group at the C—H bond most prone to ionization. In support of this theory, Drummond and Waters (*J. Chem. Soc.* 1955, 497), found that the rate of oxidation of cyclohexanone by manganic pyrophosphate reached, at high concentration of the oxidant, a limiting rate which was equal to the rate of enolization of cyclohexanone. Recently, however (Littler, *J. Chem. Soc.* 1962, 832), this idea has been queried since, in strong sulphuric acid, it has been shown that both manganic and cobaltic ions can oxidize ketones at rates which are greater than those of enolization. Moreover, the study of solvent isotope effects has indicated that for those one-electron oxidants, which are effective only in the presence of mineral acid, a preliminary acid-catalysed reaction (equilibrium 2 of p. 91) does not seem to be involved. Since kinetic isotope effects can still be observed in oxidations of ketones by acid solutions of ions such as Mn^{III}, Co^{III} and V^V, concerted reactions, in which the oxidant first co-ordinates with the oxygen atom of the carbonyl group, may be involved.

In the co-ordination process the metallic ion behaves as an electron-accepting Lewis acid, and clearly such a process could occur more

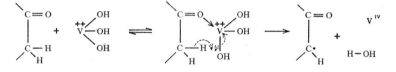

easily than the co-ordination with proton (equation 2 of p. 91) which initiates acid-catalysed enolization.

There seems to be little doubt, however, that under conditions appropriate for base-catalysis of enolization both ketones and aldehydes are oxidized by electron removal from their enol anions. This statement is certainly true for the oxidation of acyloins, such as benzoin or glucose by alkaline cupric complexes, such as are found in Fehling's solution.

The oxidation of carboxylic acids

Saturated carboxylic acids, and still more their anions, are very difficult to oxidize but the reactions which they do exhibit serve to illustrate further, by contrast, the importance of enolization in relation to oxidative processes.

The saturated monocarboxylic acids are all very resistant to heterolytic oxidation, but they can be attacked by those very active free atoms or radicals ($\cdot Cl$, $\cdot OH$, $\cdot CH_3$) which can also attack paraffin hydrocarbons (see Chapters 2 and 3). Electrolytic oxidation, which leads to decarboxylation and radical coupling,

6. $CH_3-CO_2^- \xrightarrow{-e} CH_3-CO-O\cdot \longrightarrow CO_2 + \cdot CH_3 \longrightarrow C_2H_6$

effects changes which are similar to those of the homolytic decomposition of a diacyl peroxide.

Bromination however can be effected both homolytically and heterolytically, with quite different results. If the anhydrous silver salt of a carboxylic acid is treated with a solution of bromine in carbon tetrachloride then the *Hunsdiecker reaction* occurs.

7. $R-CO_2Ag + Br_2 \longrightarrow R-Br + CO_2 + AgBr$

This involves the homolytic decomposition of an acyl hypobromite, which can be detected as an intermediate by its ability to add on to olefins (compare Prévost's reaction, p. 121). The formation of this hypobromite may be heterolytic.

8. $R-CO-O^-$ + $Br-Br$ + Ag^+ $\longrightarrow$ $R-CO-O-Br$ + $AgBr$

but the decomposition of the hypohalite is undoubtedly a homolytic chain reaction

9. $R-CO-O-Br$ $\longrightarrow$ $R-CO-O\cdot$ + $Br\cdot$

10. $R-CO-O\cdot$ $\longrightarrow$ $R\cdot$ + CO_2

11. $R\cdot$ + $Br-O-CO-R$ $\longrightarrow$ $R-Br$ + $\cdot O-CO-R$

because there is some attack on the solvent,

12. $R\cdot + CCl_4$ $\longrightarrow$ $R-Cl$ + $\cdot CCl_3$

since alkyl chlorides contaminate the resulting alkyl bromide. Again optically active α-methylbutyric acid gives racemic 2-bromo-butane,

13. $C_2H_5-CH(CH_3)-CO_2Ag + Br_2$ $\longrightarrow$ $C_2H_5-CH(CH_3)-Br$

and the reaction can be used to decarboxylate acids in which the carboxyl group is situated at the bridgehead of a rigid ring system:

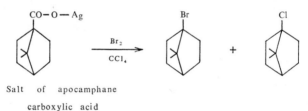

Salt   of   apocamphane

carboxylic acid

This fact shows that the bromine cannot act by a heterolytic displacement mechanism.

Heterolytic bromination of carboxylic acids, which occurs only in the α-position, is best effected by the procedure of Hell, Volhard and Zelinsky, in which the liquid acid is heated with bromine, together with a little red phosphorus, which acts as a catalyst by forming phosphorus tribromide and thence the acyl bromide. Careful studies by H. B. Watson (*Chem. Reviews*, 1930, **7**, 180) have shown that the bromination only occurs via the acid bromide, which can be regarded as a heterolytic chain transfer agent,

14. $R-CH_2-CO-Br + Br_2$ $\longrightarrow$ $R-CHBR-CO-Br$ + HBr

15. $R-CHBr-CO-Br + R-CH_2-CO_2H$

                $\rightleftharpoons$ $R-CHBr-CO_2H + R-CH_2-CO-Br$

and that the heterolytic chlorination of carboxylic acids has a similar mechanism.

In contrast to ketones, the bromination of carboxylic acids is *specifically* catalysed by hydrogen bromide or hydrogen chloride, sulphuric acid having no accelerating effect. Again hydrogen bromide acts autocatalytically in the first stage of the reaction, clearly by the equilibrium

16. $R-CH_2-CO_2H + HBr \rightleftharpoons R-CH_2-CO-Br + H_2O$

for traces of water check the reaction whilst acetic anhydride, though also a catalyst, has no immediate effect.

It appears, therefore, that the acid-catalysed enolization of a carboxylic acid does not occur, but that the enolization of the acid bromide is possible. The difference can be explained by the fact that the mesomerism of a carboxylic acid, (IX), reduces the electrophilic character of the carboxyl group whilst this is enhanced inductively by the halogen substituent in the acid bromide (X).

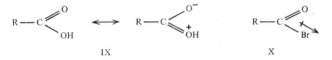

IX   X

However, again in contrast to ketones, the bromination of carboxylic acids is a reaction of first order with respect to bromine, so that if an enol (XI) is formed it must react with a halogen molecule at a measurably slow rate. Though this bromination can be written as a concerted process (compare structure II of p. 92), the inductive effect of the bromine substituent greatly diminishes the electrophilic character of the C=C bond of the enol and in this way slows down the addition process.

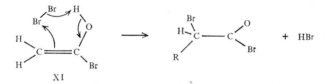

XI   + HBr

Acetic anhydride is much more ketonic in character than is acetic acid and its bromination, though particularly susceptible to hydrogen bromide catalysis,

UNIVERSITY COLLEGE LIBRARY CARDIFF

17. $CH_3-CO-O-CO-CH_3 + HBr$

$$\rightleftharpoons CH_3-CO-OH + CH_3-CO-Br$$

does exhibit general acid catalysis.

With malonic acid, however, the first stage of the bromination is a reaction of zero order with respect to bromine and the substitution can be effected in aqueous solution, so that enol formation is evidently involved. The bromination of bromo-malonic acid to dibromo-malonic acid, however, again shows the inductive effect of halogen substitution in retarding halogen addition to an enol, for it again is a reaction which is of first order with respect to bromine concentration.

Other heterolytic oxidations of malonic acid can be effected without difficulty; it is oxidized by selenium dioxide

18. $CH_2(CO_2H)_2 + SeO_2 \longrightarrow CO(CO_2H)_2 + Se + H_2O$

and also by nitrous acid. Esters and amides of malonic acid (e.g. barbituric acid and many pyrimidines) are almost as reactive as phenols towards heterolytic oxidizing and substituting agents.

Succinic acid however is only slightly more reactive than acetic acid towards all chemical oxidants, for it is resistant to such strong oxidizing agents as chromic acid and permanganate.

The homolytic oxidation of malonic acid is not difficult, and this too depends upon enolization, for a kinetic study of its oxidation by manganic pyrophosphate (Drummond and Waters *J. Chem. Soc.* 1954, 2456) shows that an intermediate complex, probably a chelate derivative of the enol, must first form.

19.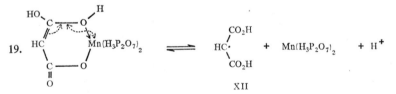

XII

The breakdown of this complex gives the radical of malonic acid, which is electrophilic enough to be an oxidizing agent, for reaction (19) is reversible and, more significantly, the slow oxidation of malonic acid by manganic pyrophosphate can promote the oxidations of alcohols and even of ethers, which are not attacked directly by manganic pyrophosphate,

20. $HO-CH_2-H + \cdot CH(CO_2H)_2 \longrightarrow HO-CH_2\cdot + H-CH(CO_2H)_2$

21. $HO-CH_2\cdot + Mn^{III} \longrightarrow O{=}CH_2 + Mn^{II} + H^+$

The radicals correspondingly derived from ethylmalonic and benzyl-malonic acids do not have this ability to attack alcohols and ethers, probably because the alkyl substituents inductively decrease the electrophilic character of the malonic acid radical, (XII).

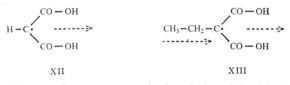

XII   XIII

In the absence of oxygen the malonic acid is oxidized by Mn^{III} to tartronic acid, which is then oxidized as an α-hydroxy-acid to gly-oxylic acid and thence to formic acid and carbon dioxide.

$$\cdot CH(CO_2H)_2 \longrightarrow HO—CH(CO_2H)_2 \longrightarrow CO_2 + O{=}CH—CO_2H$$
$$O{=}CH—CO_2H \longrightarrow O{=}CH—OH + CO_2$$

When oxygen is present, however, it is rapidly absorbed by the malonic acid radical and the resulting peroxy radical rapidly oxidizes, through oxalic acid, to carbon dioxide, formic acid not being formed. The following scheme gives a rational picture of this degradation.

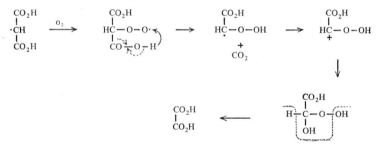

The oxidation of malonic acid by acid permanganate may well follow a similar course.

In this connection the oxidation of *oxalic acid* is worth considera-tion. This compound is *not* attacked by permanganate ions, which are good heterolytic oxidants, but is rapidly attacked by manganic ions, for if acid permanganate is treated with sufficient fluoride ions to repress, by complexing manganous ions, the Guyard reaction:

22. $(MnO_4)^- + 4Mn^{2+} + 8H^+ \rightleftharpoons 5Mn^{3+} + 4H_2O$

which in acid solution is a rapid equilibrium, then oxalic acid–per-manganate mixtures can be stored unchanged for days. Again, in strongly alkaline solutions, oxalate is the stable end-product of the permanganate oxidations of nearly all organic compounds (Drummond and Waters, *J. Chem. Soc.* 1953, 435). The oxidation of oxalic acid by manganic ions is kinetically complex, for it involves the formation of mangani-oxalate complexes, e.g. $Mn(HC_2O_4)_3$, and may involve some electron transfer between two manganic ions similar to that involved in the oxidation of cobaltic oxalate by ceric ions (p. 55). However, an intermediate free radical, which may be either (XIV) or (XV), is undoubtedly liberated,

23.

$$\bar{O}-\underset{\underset{O}{\|}}{C}-\underset{\underset{O}{\|}}{C}-\bar{O} \quad \xrightarrow{-e} \quad \dot{O}-\underset{\underset{O}{\|}}{C}-\underset{\underset{O}{\|}}{C}-\bar{O} \quad \longrightarrow \quad O=\underset{\underset{O}{\|}}{C} + \cdot\underset{\underset{O}{\|}}{C}-\bar{O}$$

XIV   XV

and this is a strong reducing agent for the reduction of mercuric chloride to mercurous chloride by oxalic acid can be initiated by the addition of a little manganic salt, or of unprotected permanganate.

The oxalic acid–mercuric chloride reaction is an interesting chain process, depending upon the production of the active mercurous ion Hg^+ (*J.A.C.S.* 1941, **63**, 906):

24. $(C_2O_4)^- + Hg^{2+} \longrightarrow Hg^+ + 2CO_2$ ⎫
25. $Hg^+ + (C_2O_4)^{2-} \longrightarrow Hg + (C_2O_4)^-$ ⎬ *chain*
26. $Hg + Hg^{2+} \longrightarrow (Hg_2)^{2+}$ ⎭

The biochemical oxidation of acids

The outstanding differences between chemical and biochemical oxidation processes are best exemplified by reference to carboxylic acids, which can easily be oxidized to carbon dioxide by living cells but are, in neutral aqueous solution, inert to chemical oxidizing agents.

The difference between chemical and biochemical mechanisms is however far less than would appear at first sight, for the oxidation of acetic acid by biochemical processes is due to its participation in the *Krebs cycle* of reversible chemical changes, whilst the oxidation of higher fatty acids involves enzymic reactions of a closely similar type.

The Krebs cycle is customarily written as shown on p. 105, though since the reactions occur at pH 6–7 *one* of the carboxyl groups of each of the polybasic acids concerned must be ionized, or associated with a metallic cation that is co-ordinated into the enzyme catalyst.

The Krebs cycle for the oxidation of acetate

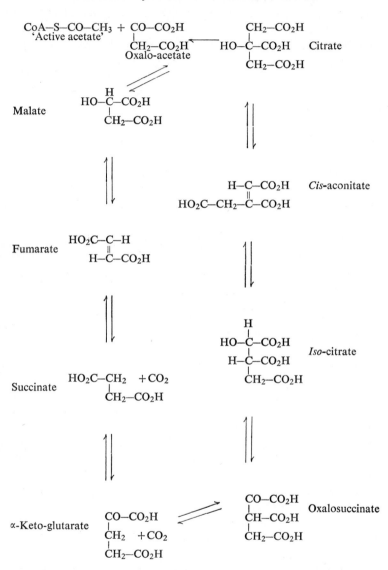

The latter hypothesis is the more probable, since it can help to explain the stereospecificity of enzyme reactions.

In the first stage of the biochemical oxidation of acetate, an acetate anion must reversibly condense with *Coenzyme-A*, which is known to be a thiol (usually written as CoA-SH), to form a reactive thio-ester.

27. $CoA—SH + {}^-O—CO—CH_3 \rightleftharpoons CoA—S—Co—CH_3 + OH^-$

The 'active acetate' so formed then condenses with oxalo-acetic acid, by a process resembling the synthesis of acetoacetic ester from ethyl acetate by the Claisen condensation, giving enzymically bound citric acid. The latter then isomerizes, by dehydration to *cis*-aconitic acid and addition of water in the reverse direction to *iso*-citric acid, which is an easily oxidized α-hydroxy-acid. The enzymic oxidation of compounds of this type, which is effected by hydride transfer to a pyridine ring, has been discussed on p. 70 and has simple chemical analogues amongst oxidations of alcohols.

The further stages of oxidation from oxalo-succinic acid to succinic acid can all be paralleled by simple non-enzymic reactions, but as yet the enzymic oxidation of succinic acid to fumaric acid cannot be correlated with any known chemical reaction. Biochemical evidence indicates that it is a hydride transfer reaction involving a flavine nucleotide. The remaining reactions which convert fumaric acid to oxalo-acetic acid are similar to those involved in the oxidation of aconitic acid.

Labelling by ${}^{14}C$ has shown that the Krebs cycle does not involve *free* citric acid, which has two identical $—CH_2—CO_2H$ groups, for the group which is oxidized is the one which has been derived from the original acetate; the other must be bound to the enzyme system. Binding at one point is sufficient to make the whole reaction stereospecific. Essentially, it is the enzymically bound oxalo-acetic acid, $HO_2C—CO—CH_2—CO_2$-Enzyme, which acts as a carrier for the oxidation of acetate by providing a bound but reactive carbonyl group with which the ester 'Acetyl Co-enzyme A' can condense. In this bound oxalo-acetic acid the carbon centre of the carbonyl group is very strongly electrophilic because both the free, unionized, carboxyl group and the bound carboxylate inductively attract electrons from the carbon centre.

Further evidence concerning the role of citrate in the Krebs cycle comes from the study of the toxic action of the fluoro-acetate anion,

$(FCH_2—CO_2)^-$, (R. A. Peters, *Advances in Enzymology*, 1957, **18**, 113; *Biochem. J.* 1959, **72**, 11P). This ion can combine enzymically with oxalo-acetate to give fluoro-citrate, but the latter does not then give an aconitate, but blocks the enzyme responsible for the dehydration of citrate.

The reason why fluoro-citrate does not give a fluoro-aconitate can be seen from inspection of its structural formula. The fluorine atom, though bound too strongly to carbon for hydrolysis to fluoride anion to be possible, is a very strong electron-attracting group. Now the dehydration of citrate to *cis*-aconitate requires the release of a hydroxyl anion to be an electron movement away from a $—CH_2—CO_2H$ group.

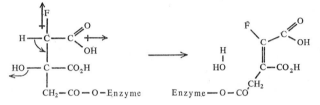

In a fluoro-citrate this elimination would be prevented by the strong electron attraction of the fluorine atom in the opposite direction. Fluoro-citrate probably combines easily with the enzyme that is concerned in the dehydration of citrate, but since no chemical reaction can then follow the complex is inactive and unable to attack citrate which in consequence accumulates to such an extent that the whole metabolic system is disordered.

The oxidation of higher fatty acids also involves Co-enzyme-A together with reactions closely similar to those of the Krebs cycle. By the use of the isotopically-labelled forms of acetic acid, $^{14}CH_3—CO_2H$ and $CH_3—^{14}CO_2H$, it has been shown that long-chain acids are both built up and degraded by two-carbon units through a process resembling the synthesis of acetoacetic ester:

28. $CH_3—CO—S—CoA + H—CH_2—CO—S—CoA$
$$\rightleftharpoons CH_3—CO—CH_2—CO—S—CoA + HS—CoA$$

The oxidation of a long-chain fatty acid is first noticed at the β-carbon atom, and of course is a reversible reaction

29. $R—CH_2—CH_2—CH_2—CH_2—CO_2H$
$$\rightleftharpoons R—CH_2—CH_2—CO—CH_2—CO_2H$$

similar to the oxidation of succinic acid to oxalo-acetic acid in the Krebs cycle. The formation of an $\alpha\beta$-unsaturated acid is thought to be an intermediate stage in this process. Acetylenic acids are abundant in fungi, and are found in many plants; these might be formed from the keto-acids.

CHAPTER 8

The Oxidation of Unsaturated Compounds and Aromatic Hydrocarbons

The π-electrons of olefins and acetylenes are more loosely held to their carbon nuclei than are the electron pairs of single bonds, and they are accessible to direct attack by electrophilic reagents. However, the two sets of π-electrons of acetylenes are each held more firmly between the carbon nuclei than are the π-electrons of olefins: actually the triple bond, $C\equiv C$, is decidedly electrophilic in character, as evidenced by the degree of acidity of compounds of types $R-C\equiv C-H$ and $R-C\equiv C-CO_2H$. Consequently, acetylenes are less easy to oxidize than olefins and differential oxidation can be achieved with molecules that contain groups of both of these types. When oxidations of acetylenes do occur, however, they appear throughout to be similar in type to oxidations of olefins.

Cyclic groups of delocalized π-electrons occur in aromatic and heterocyclic compounds and these again are more firmly held into the whole molecule than are the π-electrons of isolated $C=C$ bonds. So much is this the case, that the resistance of such molecules towards strong oxidants like chromic acid or permanganate can be taken as a measure of their 'aromatic character'. However, polycyclic aromatic compounds, as a group, have structures in which, at certain points, there is a much greater degree of π-electron localization than is the case in benzene and these compounds can more easily be oxidized. Conversely, pyridine rings are less easily oxidized than benzene rings because nitrogen is more electrophilic than CH and so hinders electron removal.

It should be recognized that the first stage (I) of an aromatic substitution (whether homolytic or heterolytic) is an addition to the organic molecule of a powerful electrophilic reagent and so is, in fact, an oxidation. In the following reaction the benzene sulphonic acid, formed by the elimination (II), has the same oxidation level as phenol.

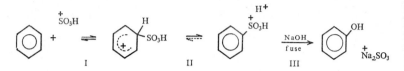

With benzene derivatives the speed of the proton elimination (II) leads to substitution rather than to addition but, as many studies of halogenation of higher aromatic hydrocarbons have shown, polycyclic aromatic compounds behave much more like olefins and addition to the initial cation (IV) can occur. Further oxidation of the alcoholic intermediate (V) would then occur rapidly to give a quinone.

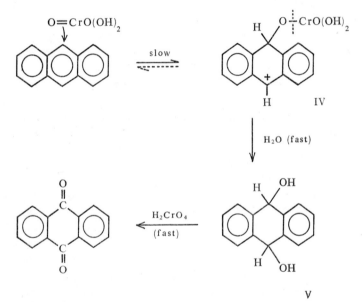

Addition to the carbonium ion (IV) is favoured because this has a positive charge which is much more localized than that in the corresponding ion, (I), of a benzene derivative.

Homolytic oxidation of olefins

The *autoxidation* of olefinic substances has been dealt with in Chapter 2 in which it was explained that peroxy radicals, R—O—O·, tended to remove hydrogen from allylic systems,

$$-CH_2-CH=CH- + RO_2\cdot \longrightarrow RO_2-H + -\overset{\cdot}{C}H-CH=CH-$$

because the formation of a mesomeric radical in this way usually required less activation energy than did radical addition to the double bond. The latter reaction does occur at moderate temperatures with compounds such as styrene which have no allylic C—H groups, with conjugated dienes which yield mesomeric radicals thereby and, at elevated temperatures, it becomes a noticeable concurrent reaction with olefins of other types. Autoxidation occurs less easily with acetylenes than with olefins. Allylic oxidation again occurs quite easily with groups such as

$$-\overset{|}{C}H-CH{=}N{-}, \qquad -\overset{|}{C}H-N{=}N{-}$$

(e.g. hydrazones) and of course with —CH—CO (ketones, Chapter 7).

Allylic substitution by halogenating agents was also discussed in Chapter 2 and it was pointed out that C—H attack was best effected by reagents, such as N-bromo-succinimide or tertiary butyl hypochlorite which initially yielded traces of halogen atoms but thereafter continued chain reactions through other radicals, e.g. Me_3C—O• or R_2N• which were excellent hydrogen-abstracting reagents with but little tendency to add to C=C bonds. However, if halogen atoms and halogen molecules are present in significant concentration then homolytic addition can be effected at double bonds quite as easily as, and often more rapidly than, heterolytic addition.

The simplest way to effect homolytic halogenation is of course by photochemical activation. With chlorine this is usually a chain reaction, as kinetic studies have shown, for it is retarded by the presence of oxygen, which would combine with the intermediate organic radical.

1. $R_2C{=}CH_2 + Cl\cdot \longrightarrow R_2\overset{\cdot}{C}{-}CH_2{-}Cl$

2. $R_2\overset{\cdot}{C}{-}CH_2{-}Cl + Cl_2 \longrightarrow R_2C(Cl){-}CH_2{-}Cl + \cdot Cl$

In this connection the photochemical chlorination of benzene is of interest. It occurs rapidly, does not require irradiation by light of high intensity for it involves long reaction chains, and gives a mixture of the stereoisomers of benzene hexachloride, $C_6H_6Cl_6$. If maleic anhydride is added the adducts (VI) and (VII) can also be formed, (p. 112).

With bromine the equivalent reaction to (1) is almost thermoneutral and so is reversible. For this reason bromine atoms catalyse $cis \rightleftharpoons trans$ isomerizations, e.g. of maleic to fumaric acid.

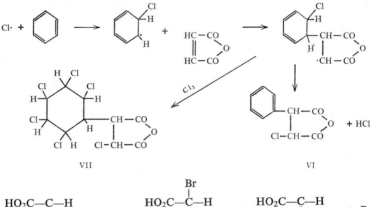

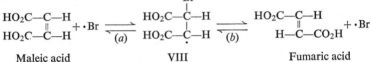

Maleic acid   VIII   Fumaric acid

Free rotation can occur about the single C—C bond of the intermediate radical (VIII) which tends to turn into its most stable conformation. With the example illustrated above the forward addition
(a) to maleic acid is exothermic, but the addition of bromine to
fumaric acid (b) is slightly endothermic, so that the equilibrium shifts
from maleic acid to give the thermodynamically more stable fumaric
acid. This isomerization, which does not occur in the heterolytic
bromination of olefins, can be used as a diagnostic test for the presence
of bromine atoms in liquid phase oxidations. Again, homolytic
bromine addition to the radical (VIII) gives a mixture of isomerides
of $\alpha\beta$-dibromosuccinic acid, the thermodynamically more stable one
(meso) preponderating, whilst the heterolytic additions of bromine
to maleic and fumaric acid are different stereospecific processes.

The iodination of olefins can be effected photochemically but each
stage of the reaction sequence is reversible and so the photolysis of
1,2-di-iodo-compounds can lead to elimination of the halogen.

3. I_2 $\rightleftharpoons$ $2I\cdot$

4. $I\cdot + CH_2{=}CH_2$ $\rightleftharpoons$ $I—CH_2—CH_2\cdot$

5. $I\cdot + I—CH_2—CH_2—I$ $\rightleftharpoons$ $I—I + \cdot CH_2—CH_2—I$

A similar heterolytic elimination can be brought about by iodide
anions in an ionizing solvent

and so iodine cannot be used as an effective oxidant for olefins.

Another group of oxidizing free radicals, which can be added to olefinic bonds, comprises the monomeric oxides of nitrogen, NO and NO$_2$. Nitrogen dioxide, at room temperature, exists mainly as the dimer, nitrogen tetroxide, N$_2$O$_4$, and since the main products of the addition of nitrogen dioxide to simple olefins have turned out to be nitro-nitrites, (IX), which are easily hydrolysed to nitro-alcohols (X)

$$IX \qquad \begin{matrix} R_2C \!-\!\!-\!\!-\! CR_2' \\ | \qquad\quad | \\ O\!=\!N\!\rightarrow\!O \quad O\!-\!N\!=\!O \end{matrix} \qquad \begin{matrix} R_2C \!-\!\!-\!\!-\! CR_2' \\ | \qquad\quad | \\ O\!=\!N\!\rightarrow\!O \quad O\!-\!H \end{matrix} \qquad X$$

it was, for a long time, thought that this reaction was heterolytic. It was surmised that nitrogen tetroxide might dissociate heterolytically (6) as well as homolytically and that heterolytic ionization would be followed immediately by the electrophilic addition of the nitronium ion, NO$_2^+$, to an olefin according to Markownikow's rule, and that subsequently the more stable nitrite anion would add, by way of its oxygen atom, to the carbonium ion thus formed:

6. $N_2O_4 \qquad\qquad\qquad \rightleftharpoons (NO_2)^+ + (NO_2)^-$

7. $R_2C{=}CH_2 + NO_2^+ \qquad\qquad \longrightarrow R_2\overset{+}{C}{-}CH_2{-}NO_2$

8. $O{=}N{-}O^- + R_2\overset{+}{C}{-}CH_2{-}NO_2 \longrightarrow O{=}N{-}O{-}CR_2{-}CH_2{-}NO_2$

However, the addition of nitrogen tetroxide to olefins can only be effected smoothly in non-ionizing solvents, for otherwise complications due to the formation of nitric and nitrous acids arise. Recent evidence indicates that in dry ether at 0° the reaction is mainly homolytic, for the addition of nitrogen tetroxide to methyl acrylate gives a mixture which, after hydrolysis by water, yields β-nitromethyl acrylate and methyl α-hydroxy-β-nitropropionate together with polymer (Schlechter and Conrad, *J.A.C.S.* 1953, **75**, 5620). This corresponds to homolytic addition and is quite inconsistent with any reactions involving NO$_2^+$.

Again, if the reaction between cyclohexene and nitrogen tetroxide

9.

$$MeO-CO-CH=CH_2 + NO_2 \longrightarrow MeO-CO-\overset{\cdot}{C}H-CH_2-NO_2$$

$$MeO-CO-CH=CH-NO_2 \quad \nwarrow$$

$$MeO-CO-CH=CH-NO_2 \quad \searrow \quad MeO-CO-CH-CH_2-NO_2$$

$$MeO-CO-CH(OH)-CH_2-NO_2 \quad \swarrow \qquad \underset{O-NO}{\overset{|}{}}$$

is carried out in the presence of bromotrichloromethane then 1-bromo-2-nitrocyclohexane and 1-bromo-2-chlorocyclohexane form the main addition products (Brand and Stevens, *Chem. & Ind.* 1956, 469)

10 $-CH{=}CH- + \cdot NO_2 \longrightarrow \cdot\overset{|}{C}H-\overset{|}{C}H-NO_2$

11. $Cl_3C-Br + \cdot\overset{|}{C}H-\overset{|}{C}H-NO_2 \longrightarrow Cl_3C\cdot + Br-\overset{|}{C}H-\overset{|}{C}H-NO_2$

The chlorine substitution evidently occurs by way of the $\cdot CCl_3$ radical. The intermediate radical, $\cdot\overset{|}{C}H-\overset{|}{C}H-NO_2$, can also pick up bromine from bromoform or iodine from molecular iodine (*J.A.C.S.* 1958, **80**, 338).

Nitric oxide does not add on to olefins unless a trace of nitrogen dioxide is also present (J. F. Brown, *J.A.C.S.* 1957, **79**, 2480), but if this is the case a rapid sequence of reactions occurs, the first stage of which appears to be the addition of nitric oxide to the carbon radical formed by the prior addition of nitrogen dioxide to the olefin.

12. $Me_2C{=}CH_2 + NO_2 \longrightarrow Me_2\overset{\cdot}{C}-CH_2-NO_2$

13. $Me_2\overset{\cdot}{C}-CH_2-NO_2 + NO \longrightarrow Me_2C-CH_2-NO_2$
$$\underset{N{=}O}{\overset{|}{}}$$

Following upon this, further homolytic additions, which have analogies in the chemistry of nitroso-compounds, occur rapidly at the N=O bond of the primary addition product.

These reactions have been explored as potential oxidative routes for the conversion of simple olefins into technically useful products, but since they give complex mixtures their applicability is not very promising.

The photochemical addition of oxygen to conjugated dienes and to polycyclic aromatic compounds such as anthracene is undoubtedly a homolytic process since with several substances it has been shown that the photochemical activation has to include an energy transfer from the first excited molecule to an isomeric 'triplet state' in which two electrons are unpaired (XI). The triplet states of some such molecules have a sufficiently long life for it to be possible to record their absorption spectra, using the technique of flash photolysis, and to show, by electron spin resonance, that they are indeed di-radicals.

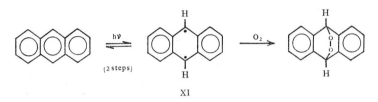

XI

Decompositions of trans-annular peroxides have been discussed in Chapter 3.

The direct attack on olefins by the cations of transition metals needs only brief mention, for it is evident that the removal of one-electron removal from a C=C bond would give a radical-cation of such high-energy content that it could be effected only by homolytic oxidants of such high redox potential that they would also attack water, or any suitable solvent.

$$-\overset{|}{C}=\overset{|}{C}- \quad \xrightarrow{\ -e\ } \quad -\overset{\bullet}{\underset{|}{C}}-\overset{+}{\underset{|}{C}}-$$

A few olefin oxidations by cobaltic ions have been examined kinetically by Bawn and his colleagues (*J. Chem. Soc.* 1957, 1854, 1867) and seem to involve direct attack on the π-bond, but few product studies have yet been made. Uncomplexed manganic ions may behave similarly, but the other oxidants of this type, described in Chapters 4–7, are so inert to olefins that radical polymerization of the latter can be used to demonstrate the presence of transient radicals from the oxidation of other substrates.

Heterolytic allylic oxidation of olefins

About 10–15 years ago it was rather naïvely thought that all allylic oxidations of olefins, and all oxidations of aromatic side-chains at C—H bonds adjacent to aromatic nuclei, were homolytic processes, but now this generalization should be treated with reserve, for several oxidants, such as selenium dioxide (Chapter 7), which have as yet exhibited no other features indicative of homolytic reactivity, do attack allylic systems. Actually, the resonance stabilization of the radical —ĊH—CH=CH—, which favours homolytic dehydrogenation, is paralleled by that of the cation, —$\overset{+}{C}H$—CH=CH—, obtainable by hydride transfer, which, as described earlier (Chapter 4), is one of the major routes of heterolytic oxidation.

The hydride transfer reactions of alcohols described in Chapter 4 were all reactions in which (H)⁻ was transferred from one carbon atom to another, but hydride transfer from carbon to oxygen is also possible for at high temperatures (100–250°) *quinones* can directly effect the dehydrogenation of allylic compounds like 1,4-dihydronaphthalene, the aromatization of partly hydrogenated substances such as tetralin or tetrahydrocarbazole (XII) and the selective oxidation to aldehydes of allylic and benzylic alcohols (*J. Chem. Soc.* 1954, 3548; 1956, 3070; 1960, 3116 etc.).

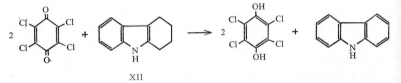

XII

The best reagent to use is a quinone of high redox potential, such as chloranil, tetrachloro-*ortho*-benzoquinone or a dichloro-dicyano-benzoquinone, all of which have electrophilic substituents which enhance the electrophilic action of the carbonyl groups. The initial reaction is a bimolecular transfer of hydrogen, with two electrons, from a C—H bond to the oxygen atom of the quinone, to give a carbonium ion and the anion of a quinol.

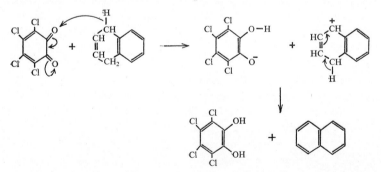

Very good evidence for the transient existence of the intermediate carbonium ion has been obtained by the dehydrogenation of 1,1-dimethyltetralin, which yielded 1,2-dimethylnaphthalene by a Wagner–

Meerwein rearrangement of an intermediate cation (*J. Chem. Soc.* 1960, 3133).

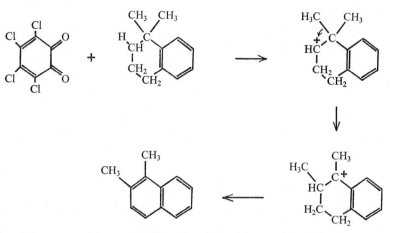

However, with some olefins, heating with an *ortho*-quinone may lead to a heterolytic addition instead.

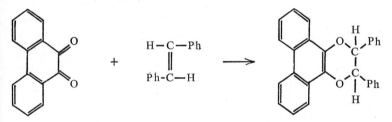

These dehydrogenations can be contrasted with the photochemically activated homolytic dehydrogenations that can be effected by quinones under quite different experimental conditions (p. 24).

Other oxygen compounds, as for instance aromatic nitro-compounds, can be used as hydrogen acceptors and many of these hydride transfers can be carried out quite easily on the surface of an active palladium, platinum or nickel catalyst. A particularly interesting example is the reduction of maleic acid to succinic acid by cyclohexene in the presence of palladium at 65°

Perhaps this reaction is mechanistically similar to the biochemical equilibrium between fumaric and succinic acids (p. 106), but the exact nature of surface-catalysed reactions is still problematical and is quite outside the scope of this book.

It is possible that the oxidation of substances such as toluene by chromic acid, chromyl chloride or permanganate may occur by hydride transfer, though evidence that some homolytic hydrogen transfer is involved in the case of chromic acid oxidations of hydrocarbons has been given in an earlier chapter. Other examples of allylic oxidation, which undoubtedly involve mesomeric cations, are given on later pages which deal with heterolytic oxidants that directly attack olefinic bonds.

Heterolytic oxidations at C=C double bonds

The direct oxidation of an olefin to an epoxide (p. 42) and the addition of molecular bromine to give a bromonium ion (p. 92) afford the simplest examples of the regular mode of attack of a two-electron abstracting agent upon an olefinic π-bond.

It has already been pointed out that the attack of a halogen molecule on the π-bond of a cyclic olefin occurs axially and leads to the formation of a *trans*-dibromide. In a rigid molecule this dibromide has a *diaxial* configuration, e.g. (XIII) which is thermodynamically less stable than the *diequatorial* configuration (XIV) in which the bromine atoms are more widely separated from the neighbouring substituent groups.

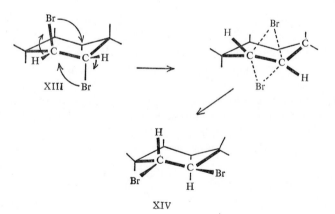

On heating above 100° for some time the less stable diaxial isomer changes to the more stable isomer, and this is an intramolecular rearrangement in which the bromine atoms move simultaneously from one carbon atom to another. Thus in the steroid series the diaxial chlorobromide (XV) isomerizes to the diequatorial chlorobromide (XVI) (Alt and Barton, *J. Chem. Soc.* 1954, 4284).

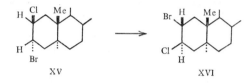

The great experimental drawback to the use of a halogen as an oxidant for olefins is, of course, the difficulty of hydrolysis of the product. With 1,2-dibromides this can be particularly troublesome since if strong alkali is used then bimolecular elimination (E2) is favoured on account of the inductive effect of the bromine atom which is less easily ionized.

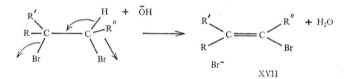

Once a bromo-olefin (XVII) has been produced the remaining halogen is too strongly bonded to carbon for displacement by nucleophilic hydrolysis. With dilute aqueous alkali the hydrolysis of *trans*-1,2-dihalides occurs via epoxide formation and this can lead to an inversion of the original configuration about each carbon centre.

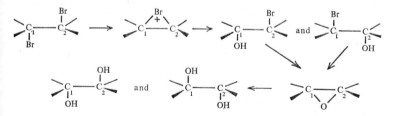

Silver acetate in acetic acid is a useful reagent for displacing chlorine or bromine atoms from alkyl halides without effecting any elimination

of a hydrogen halide, for the halide ions are then removed solvolytic-
ally and immediately trapped as their insoluble silver salts. Winstein
and Buckles (*J.A.C.S.* 1942, **64**, 2780–2796) have shown that this
reaction can be controlled to give either *cis-* or *trans-* reaction products, as desired, from *trans*-1,2-dibromides. If *trans*-1,2-dibromo-
cyclohexane is treated with silver acetate in *dry* acetic acid or acetic
anhydride the final product is *trans*-1,2-diacetoxy-cyclohexane, but
if moist acetic acid is used as the solvent then *cis*-1-hydroxy-2-acetoxy-
cyclohexane results. Each of these can easily be hydrolysed by alkali
to the corresponding cyclohexane-diol without any further change of
configuration. Winstein has explained these results by postulating the
participation of neighbouring groups. Thus the first product of
solvolysis of the *trans*-dibromide (XVIII) is not a carbonium ion but
the bromonium ion (XIX), and this then reacts with acetate anions
to give the *trans*-bromo-acetoxy compound (XX) which can be
isolated.

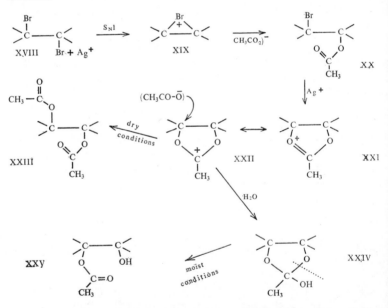

Again solvolysis of (XX) gives the cation (XXI), which alternatively
could be written as (XXII), in which the acetate group joins at two
carbon centres to give a cyclic, symmetrical structure corresponding
to that of an epoxide, or of a bromonium ion. Attack on this cation

by acetate anions again is a bimolecular process which gives the *trans*-diacetate (XXIII), but in the presence of a little water the cation (XXII) forms the neutral molecule (XXIV) which can be regarded as an *ortho*-ester and this hydrolyses so as to give the *cis*-hydroxy-acetate (XXV).

Many of the difficulties attending the oxidation of olefins to 1,2-glycols can be avoided by using *Prévost's reagents* – a solution of iodine in carbon tetrachloride together with an equivalent of silver benzoate or of silver acetate. Under anhydrous conditions this oxidant directly yields the diacyl derivative of a *trans*-glycol. The oxidizing mixture, which is very similar to that used in Hunsdiecker's reaction (p. 99), acts by the initial formation of an acyl hypoiodite, which then attacks the olefin to give an iodonium cation (XXVI). The latter is then attacked by the silver salt to give a *trans*-product by the reactions which have been described above.

$$I—I \quad + \quad Ag—O—CO—Ph \quad \longrightarrow \quad I—O—CO—Ph \quad + \quad AgI$$

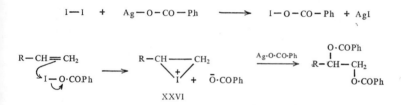

XXVI

The value of this reagent depends upon its specificity, for whilst an acyl hypohalite is a strong electrophilic reagent, free iodine, under these conditions, hardly affects other sensitive groups in a complex molecule.

Mercuric acetate, followed by iodine, can also be used for the selective oxidation of olefins: in this case the initial product seems to be a π-complex of mercury (XXVII) rather than an iodonium cation (Chatt, *Chem. Reviews*, 1951, **48**, 1).

XXVII

A similar picture can be advanced to explain the course of oxidation of olefins by *lead tetra-acetate* and by thallic acetate. (See R. Criegee, *Angewandte Chem.* 1958, **70**, 173: Whitham, *J. Chem. Soc.* 1961, 2232.)

9

In hot solutions lead tetra-acetate undoubtedly acts as a homolytic oxidant at allylic or benzylic positions of hydrocarbons, e.g.

$$Ph-CH_3 + Pb(O-COCH_3)_4$$
$$\longrightarrow Ph-CH_2-O-COCH_3 + CO_2 + CH_4 + Pb(O-COCH_3)_2$$

for the reaction products include both carbon dioxide and methane, substances which must originate from the reactions

$$CH_3-CO-O\cdot \longrightarrow CH_3\cdot + CO_2 \quad \text{and} \quad CH_3\cdot + H-R \longrightarrow CH_4 + \cdot R$$

but, at or near room temperature lead tetra-acetate, in acetic acid or benzene, attacks olefinic bonds directly and no carbon dioxide is evolved, so that it must act heterolytically. Criegee has represented this oxidation as a reaction which follows slight ionization of the lead tetra-acetate in the sense

$$Pb(O-COCH_3)_4 \rightleftharpoons \{Pb(O-COCH_3)_3\}^+ + (O-COCH_3)^-$$

and considers that the lead cation is the electrophilic oxidant, adding to the π-bond to give a cation that could be written either as a carbonium ion (XXVIII) or as a π-complex (XXIX).

Neutralization of this cation would then give, though an acetate (XXX), the cyclic cation (XXXI), to which reference has already

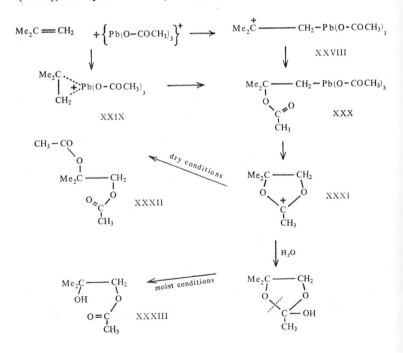

been made, for if the reagent is used under perfectly dry conditions the *trans*-diacetate (XXXII) is formed, but in moist acetic acid the *cis*-hydroxy-acetate is the end-product (XXXIII).

However, the evidence for the formation of a transient organo-lead intermediate is uncertain and a far simpler picture of the initial oxidation is that of a concerted reaction which could give the cyclic acetate complex directly.

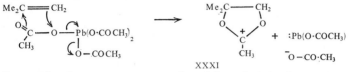

XXXI

Intramolecular rearrangements often follow the initial step of these oxidations and these may simulate allylic attack. The following are typical examples.

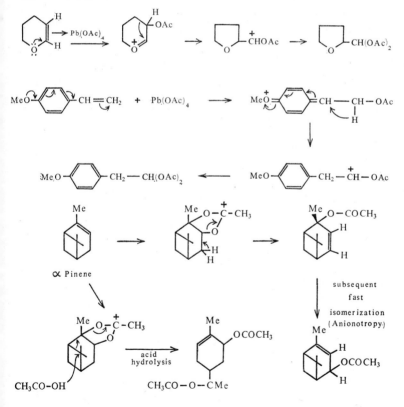

Chromic acid and *chromyl chloride* too have been shown to attack olefins by direct electrophilic attack, through one oxygen atom, on the π-electrons. Thus, in carbon tetrachloride, chromyl chloride rapidly adds to cyclohexene to give $C_6H_{10}CrO_2Cl_2$ and then $C_6H_{10}(CrO_2Cl_2)_2$, which may be written as epoxy-salts (XXXIV) and (XXXV), since on addition of water they yield *trans*-2-chloro-cyclohexanol.

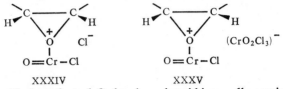

XXXIV   XXXV

The oxidation of an olefin by chromic acid is usually carried out in acetic acid, acetic anhydride, or sulphuric acid solution and is more difficult to effect than the oxidation of a primary or secondary alcohol. The oxidations are acid catalysed and so may involve mixed anhydrides, or perhaps the cation $(HCrO_3)^+$ in which the electron-accepting property of the O=Cr bond is enhanced by the positive charge. Oxidations of higher olefins often yield complex mixtures of products, but the systematic researches of W. J. Hickinbottom have shown that the products could all be formed 'via an epoxide, 1,2-glycol, or more probably some polar intermediate easily converted into one of the latter'. The initial reaction can therefore be written as

$$R_2C = CR_2' \qquad\longrightarrow\qquad \overset{+}{R_2C} - CR_2'$$

giving a derivative of Cr^{IV} which would promptly hydrolyse at the O—Cr bond to give the conjugate acid of an epoxide. Subsequent stages can be illustrated by the following scheme which has been worked out for the oxidation of tetra-methyl ethylene.

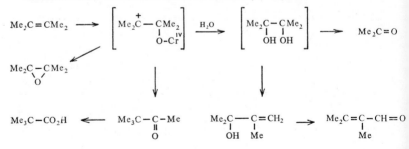

Allylic oxidation, which frequently occurs with the system

$$\begin{array}{c} C \\ \diagdown \\ C \diagup \end{array} C=\overset{|}{C}-CH_2-$$

can be explained by postulating tautomerism of the initial cation, e.g.

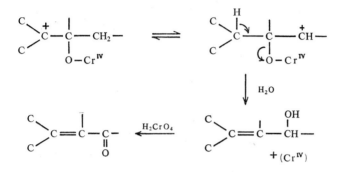

whilst oxidations of conjugated dienes to unsaturated ketones may proceed similarly.

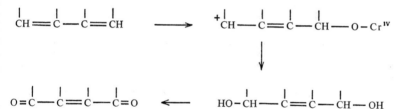

It is clear that these oxidations have many mechanistic similarities with those effected by lead tetra-acetate.

The oxidation of olefins by *permanganate* is quite different in nature, for it can be effected in neutral or alkaline solution or in solvents such as acetone and pyridine. In neutral or weakly acid solution permanganate at once converts an olefin to an acyloin and it is difficult to check still further oxidation, but in decidedly alkaline solution, of pH 12 or more, the oxidation mainly stops at the stage of formation of a *cis*-1,2-diol. The detailed reaction mechanism has been elucidated by K. Wiberg by making use of the fact that ^{18}O-labelled permanganate does not exchange its oxygen atoms with water, but yet oxidizes oleate by transferring labelled oxygen to the organic products. This work confirms earlier surmises that permanganate oxidation of olefins involves the formation of a 5-membered cyclic ring adduct (XXXVI) which then hydrolyses by Mn—O bond fission.

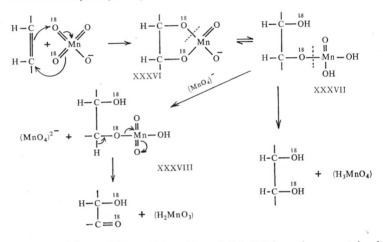

The glycol formed from oleic acid and $(Mn^{18}O_4)^-$ anions contained so much isotopically labelled oxygen that *both* hydroxyl groups had been derived from oxygen atoms originally bound to manganese.

It will be seen from the above diagram that the initial cyclic adduct (XXXVI) is necessarily a derivative of manganese-(V), and so too must be its immediate hydrolysis product (XXXVII). The direct hydrolysis of this to the glycol is viewed by Wiberg as a solvolytic reaction, since it clearly can occur quite easily in neutral aqueous solution, and like the vast majority of ester hydrolyses it must be an acyl-oxygen fission.

Acyloin formation has been supposed by him to follow the more complicated course shown, in which the manganese-(V) ester (XXXVII) is first oxidized, by permanganate, to the manganese-(VI) ester (XXXVIII) which may very well resemble the chromate ester of an alcohol (see p. 62) and would split to yield a ketone and a derivative of manganese-(IV), again by a two-electron valency change. It is necessary to postulate the oxidation step (XXXVII)→(XXXVIII) because manganese dioxide, with manganese-(IV), is the ultimate inorganic reaction product and the direct formation of an acyloin from (XXXVII) would involve the formation of manganese-(III), for which there can be no justification.

It must be remembered however that the support for this reaction mechanism depends only upon the isolation of labelled products, for the oxidation is far too rapid for kinetic study and immediately becomes a heterogeneous system in which any ion of manganese-(V) is immediately destroyed.

The great drawback to the use of permanganate as an oxidant of C=C bonds is its lack of specificity, for aldehyde, ketone and even alcohol groups can easily be oxidized by routes which have been described in previous chapters. Again, the oxidation products have to be separated from a large bulk of manganese dioxide which, as it forms, tends to adsorb a large amount of unreacted material and thereby enhances the danger of further oxidation of desirable water-soluble products.

For effecting specifically the bond fission

$$R_2C{=}CHR' \longrightarrow R_2C{=}O + R'{-}CH{=}O$$

all these difficulties have been overcome by R. Lemieux, who has introduced as an oxidant a solution of periodic acid containing just a trace of permanganate. As soon as the latter has effected the initial oxidation

$$R_2C{=}CHR' \longrightarrow R_2C(OH){-}CH(OH)R'$$

the periodic acid completes the glycol fission and, at the same time, re-oxidizes the manganese-(V) back to permanganate. For many purposes the *Lemieux reagent* has now superseded ozone as an oxidant of olefins and it has almost entirely supplanted the very expensive reagent *osmium tetroxide*.

Oxidation by the latter compound was introduced, in 1936, by R. Criegee, who found that in dry inert solvents such as ether, benzene or cyclohexane, it slowly added to olefins to give yellow products which could be decomposed by boiling with water or dilute acids giving *cis*-diols and osmic acid, H_2OsO_4.

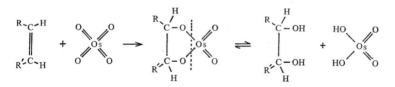

This hydrolysis is reversible and so the most satisfactory way to isolate the glycol is to effect hydrolysis in the presence of a reducing agent such as sodium sulphite or formaldehyde, when the osmic acid is converted to free osmium which can be separated and later reconverted to more osmium tetroxide. However, osmium tetroxide, like permanganate, is not a specific oxidant, for it rapidly oxidizes alcohols, phenols and amines.

Osmium tetroxide oxidation is facilitated by the addition of a tertiary base, such as pyridine, when ternary complexes (1 olefin, 1 OsO$_4$, 2 base) are formed, and then is sufficiently reactive to attack the partly localized π-bonds of higher aromatic hydrocarbons, such as phenanthrene and anthracene.

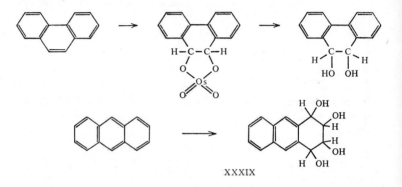

XXXIX

The anthracene adduct, on hydrolysis, broke down to give the tetrol (XXXIX) and, apart from biological reactions, this oxidation provided the first instance of attack on a double bond occurring in preference to attack at a *meso*-position of the central ring. This oxidation of anthracene indicates that the formation of ring adducts by osmium tetroxide must be a two-stage process in which a *reversible* electrophilic reaction at one carbon centre can be carried to completion by the subsequent ring closure which yields a stable covalent product, even though the initial point of attack is not that of greatest electron availability.

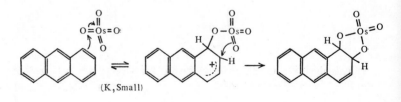

(K, Small)

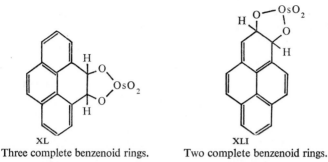

XL	XLI
Three complete benzenoid rings.	Two complete benzenoid rings.

Attack on a *meso*-position in anthracene such as that illustrated on
p. 110, could not be followed by a stereochemically favourable ring
closure, and with pyrene, on which the attack is again dissimilar to
that of reagents such as NO_2^+, the final adduct, with bonds represented
formally by (XL), has decidedly greater resonance stabilization than
(XLI) which is not formed.

The same feature regarding 'double-bond attack' on polycyclic
aromatic compounds is also significant in the elucidation of the
mechanism of *ozonization*. Though ozone is reactive enough to attack
even benzene at room temperature, Wibaut and Sixma have shown
that its reactions can be catalysed by Lewis acids such as boron
trifluoride.

$$O{=}\overset{+}{O}{-}\overset{-}{O} + BF_3 \;\rightleftharpoons\; O{=}\overset{+}{O}{-}O\overset{-}{B}F_3$$

Thus the oxidation of benzene can be regarded as a two-stage process,
the first being a reversible electrophilic addition of one of the terminal
oxygen atoms of ozone to a π-bond.

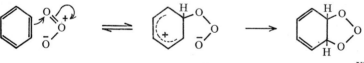

XLII

It is still uncertain whether the initial ozonides should be written
as 5-membered (XLII and XLVI) or 4-membered (XLIII) ring compounds, for the substances that can finally be isolated from the addition of ozone to olefins are either olefin–ozone co-polymers (XLIV)
of high molecular weight or else monomeric *iso*-ozonides (XLV) in
which the olefin has been separated into two fragments by the insertion
of oxygen atoms.

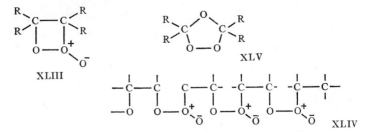

Recent work (see *Chem. Reviews*, 1958, **58**, 925) has shown that in the inert solvents that are normally used for ozonization the *iso*-ozonides are formed by the dissociation of the initial adduct into two fragments which then recombine, but in part yield some free ketone (XLVII) and some ketone peroxide (XLVIII). In the presence of water the peroxidic fragment (IL) may yield a hydroperoxide (L) identical with that obtainable by adding hydrogen peroxide to a ketone (Chapter 3), and in the presence of formaldehyde a different *iso*-ozonide (LI) may be formed.

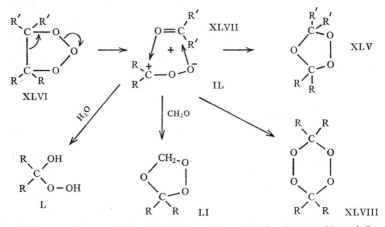

When, as is usual, it is desired to employ ozonization to effect olefin fission to simple products, e.g.

$$R_2C{=}CHR' \longrightarrow R_2C{=}O + R'{-}CHO$$

it is now customary to follow ozone addition to an organic compound by catalytic reduction with hydrogen and palladium before adding a hydrolysing solvent such as water. Over-treatment of any olefin with ozonized oxygen should be avoided for the peroxides mentioned above can break down homolytically, liberating active alkyloxy, or peroxy radicals which would of course initiate autoxidation. Ozone-catalysed autoxidation is well known; it is an almost inevitable mode of deterioration of manufactured rubber articles which have been exposed to air and sunlight.

General reading reference

BADGER, G. M., *The Structures and Reactions of the Aromatic Compounds*, Cambridge Univ. Press, 1954.

CHAPTER 9

Oxidations of Phenols and Aromatic Amines

Heterolytic oxidations

One of the characteristic properties of both phenols and aromatic amines is the rapidity with which they undergo nuclear substitution in available *ortho*- and *para*-positions by electrophilic reagents such as bromine, and in the previous chapter it was pointed out that this electrophilic substitution should be regarded as an oxidation. The oxidation of phenol by way of sulphonation and alkali fusion can be used for the preparation of quinol, but the final step is too drastic to be used in many analogous cases and it is not practicable with amines, for substances such as sulphanilic acid, $H_2N—C_6H_4—SO_3H$, are far too stable to be decomposed by heating with alkali at temperatures below that leading to complete degradation with charring. Many desired oxidation products of phenols and aromatic amines can be obtained by diazo-coupling followed by reduction to an amine and subsequent replacement of the new amine group.

Aniline can be oxidized to *p*-benzoquinone by chromic acid, but this involves a complex reaction sequence, involving the formation of a quinon-imine intermediate (aniline black), and the reaction when applied to other aromatic amines rarely gives simple products in good yield, though it was used extensively in the early days of the synthetic dyestuff industry.

Another oxidative route that merits brief mention is the conversion of phenylhydroxylamine by acid into *p*-amino-phenol. Though phenylhydroxylamine is best made by reduction of nitrobenzene and not by oxidation of aniline it is possible to oxidize primary aromatic amines, though usually in poor yield, to hydroxylamine derivatives by using per-acids, such as Caro's acid (see Chapter 3), and therefrom to obtain amino-phenols and eventually quinones.

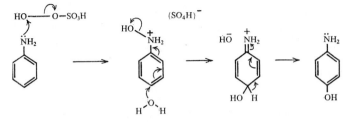

Direct oxidations of phenols by peroxides, which have been mentioned briefly in Chapter 3, are of more direct utility than direct oxidations of aromatic amines and it has only recently been established that they are heterolytic and not homolytic processes.

When *p*-cresol is refluxed with benzoyl peroxide in chloroform it yields 4-benzoyloxy-3-hydroxytoluene (I) and the same product is obtained, though in poorer yield, from *m*-cresol. With other phenols, too, a benzoate group is introduced preferentially into a position *ortho* to the original hydroxyl (Cosgrove and Waters, *J. Chem. Soc.* 1949, 3189).

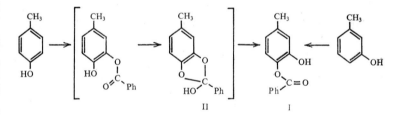

Since chloroform is a non-ionizing solvent it was thought that benzoyloxy radicals, Ph—CO—O·, might be involved, but a kinetic study by Walling and Hodgdon (*J.A.C.S.* 1958, **80**, 229) has shown that the reaction is a simple bimolecular process involving the O—H group of the phenol, for if this hydrogen is replaced by deuterium the reaction velocity decreases ($k_H/k_D = 1·32$). Again. D. B. and D. Z. Denney (*J.A.C.S.* 1960, **82**, 1389) have shown that if benzoyl peroxide is prepared from ^{18}O-labelled benzoyl chloride,

$$\overset{18O}{\underset{\parallel}{Ph—C—Cl}}$$

so as to have ^{18}O only in its carbonyl groups, then 85 % of the isotopic oxygen remains in the carbonyl group of the benzoate substituent that is introduced into the phenol. Hence homolysis of benzoyl peroxide:

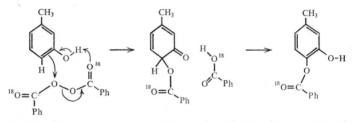

cannot occur.

The *ortho*-substitution can be explained by means of the following concerted reaction mechanism,

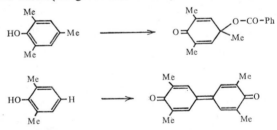

and the fact that both *para*- and *meta*-cresol give the same reaction product can be explained by supposing that a trans-esterification through a common intermediate (II) occurs, for many similar interchanges of acyl groups are known (see IV → V below).

When the *ortho*-positions of a phenol are blocked then the following oxidations occur (Cosgrove and Waters, *J. Chem. Soc.* 1951, 388).

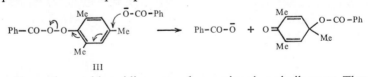

These have been explained by Walling by postulating the intermediate formation of a peroxy-ester (III) which would be prone to electrophilic attack at the *para*-position.

Benzoyl peroxide oxidizes secondary amines in a similar way. Thus isotopically labelled benzoyl peroxide reacts with dibenzylamine to give dibenzylhydroxylamine:

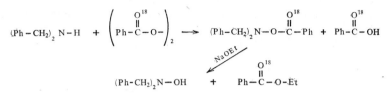

whilst diphenylamine gives benzoyl *ortho*-hydroxy-diphenylamine, (V),

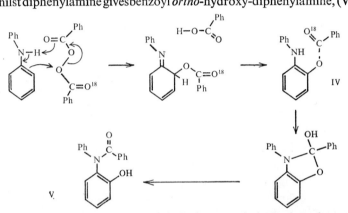

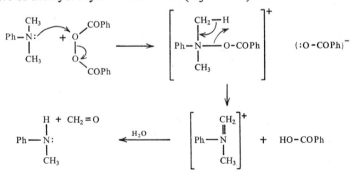

though this does contain some labelled oxygen in its hydroxyl group.

Benzoyl peroxide, and per-acids, can also effect the dealkylation of tertiary amines. This too can be represented as a heterolytic process, passing through a quaternary salt which can be regarded as a derivative of the hydroxylammonium ion $(H_3N\!-\!OH)^+$.

However, a homolytic reaction sequence, in which a C—H bond adjacent to the nitrogen atom is the initial point of attack, would be expected to lead to similar final products.

The Elbs' oxidation of phenols by potassium persulphate in cold aqueous alkali is clearly another heterolytic reaction though it was once thought to be homolytic. The first product is a hydroxyphenyl potassium sulphate (VI) which hydrolyses immediately the solution is acidified.

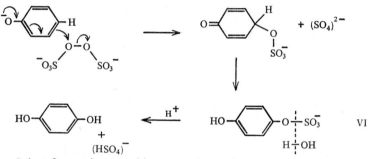

Salts of organic per-acids cannot be used successfully for this oxidation, for the reaction depends upon the elimination of the anion of a *strong* acid, $(HSO_4)^-$, when the nucleophilic phenol anion attacks the peroxide link.

Another phenol oxidant of similar electrophilic character is *lead tetra-acetate*; its reaction products with numerous phenols have been studied in detail by F. Wessely and his colleagues in Vienna. (For a review see J. D. Loudon, *Progress in Organic Chemistry*, 1961, **5**, 50). It is used in cold glacial acetic acid and again tends to introduce acetoxy groups predominantly into positions *ortho* to the original phenolic hydroxyl, yielding quinone or dienone acetates. As with the oxidations of olefins by lead tetra-acetate (Chapter 8), this *ortho*-oxidation can be represented as a concerted process, the second stage of which must be the more rapid.

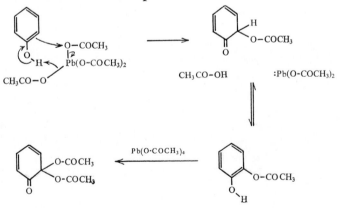

The *ortho*-attack may occur even if an alkyl substituent is present, for o-cresol gives (VII), but *para*-attack can also occur for p-cresol yields both (VIII) and (IX).

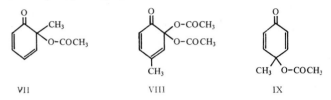

VII   VIII   IX

The analogy between these oxidations and the heterolytic oxidations of ketones which have been considered in Chapter 7 is obvious. Many interesting rearrangement products have been formed from these dienones by treatment with mineral or Lewis acid catalysts.

For example the product (VII) from *ortho*-cresol gives the resorcinol derivative (X) on treatment with acetic anhydride and a little concentrated sulphuric acid, whilst (XI) gives (XII).

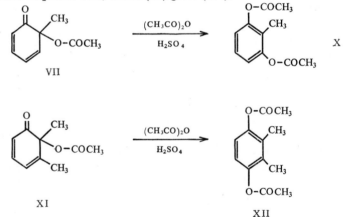

If the acetoxy group has been introduced into a blocked *para*-position then the alkyl group migrates preferentially when the dienone is hydrolysed by alkali.

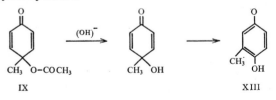

IX   XIII

10

Homolytic oxidation

Towards homolytic oxidants phenols react either by loss of the hydrogen atom of the OH group or by loss of one electron from the corresponding anion to give a resonance-stabilized free aryloxy radical (XIV)

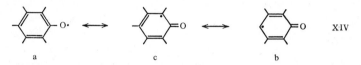

Aromatic amines give arylamine radicals of comparable stability.

It is on account of the stability, and therefore comparatively low reactivity, of such radicals that phenols and aromatic amines are potent inhibitors of autoxidation (Chapter 2): reactions such as (1) and (2) are decidedly exothermic and very rapid, and the resulting radicals are not reactive enough to remove hydrogen from C—H bonds.

1. $R\!-\!O\!-\!O\cdot + H\!-\!O\!-\!C_6H_5 \longrightarrow R\!-\!O\!-\!O\!-\!H + \cdot O\!-\!C_6H_5$

2. $R\!-\!O\!-\!O\cdot + :NR_2\!-\!C_6H_5 \longrightarrow (R\!-\!O\!-\!O:)^- + (\cdot NR_2\!-\!C_6H_5)^+$

Identical radicals can be obtained by oxidizing alkaline solutions of many phenols with potassium ferricyanide;

3. $\{Fe(CN)_6\}^{3-} + {}^-(:O\!-\!C_6H_5) \longrightarrow \{Fe(CN)_6\}^{4-} + \cdot O\!-\!C_6H_5$

or by attacking acid solutions of phenols with one-electron oxidants of somewhat higher redox potential, as for example by ceric salts. With *ortho* and *para* dihydric phenols, electron transfers such as (3) can be reversible and hence thermodynamic redox potentials can be measured for Quinol $\rightleftharpoons$ Quinone equilibria by standard potentiometric methods, but the oxidizability of monohydric phenols can only be gauged roughly in terms of 'apparent redox potentials' which refer essentially to the oxidizing powers of suitable inorganic oxidants. The difficulty here arises on account of further fast reactions of free aryloxy radicals which are discussed below.

The modern physical technique of 'electron spin resonance spectroscopy' (usually abbreviated to E.S.R.) can be applied so as to give valuable information concerning the electronic structure of any free radical that has a reasonable lifetime and has proved to be particularly valuable in obtaining information concerning both aryloxy and arylamino free radicals (Stone and Waters, *Proc. Chem. Soc.* 1962,

253). In aqueous solution the phenoxy radical itself has a mean life-time of about 10^{-3} second and so its E.S.R. spectrum can be recorded only by using a flow technique in which a solution of phenol is mixed with a solution of a suitable oxidant about 10^{-2} second before the re-acting mixture passes rapidly through the measurement cell of an E.S.R. spectrometer. A record of the E.S.R. spectrum of the free phenoxy radical (XIV) obtained in this way is shown on p. 140.

The spectrum indicates the precise values of applied magnetic fields at which quantized energy absorptions or emissions within the free radical can be made to occur by means of a micro-wave radiation of fixed frequency. A single electron should show this energy transfer, termed 'electron spin resonance' only when the energy, $h\nu$, of the micro-waves is equal to $g.H.\mu$, where H is the magnitude of the magnetic field in the region of the electron, μ is the atomic unit of magnetic moment, the Bohr magneton, and g is the 'coupling factor' that depends on the molecular environment of any unpaired electron: paired electrons have no resultant magnetic moment and so do not lead to E.S.R. spectra. For 'free' electrons there should be only one g value $= 2 \cdot 0013$, and in such circumstances the E.S.R. spectrum should consist of a single resonance line.

The spectrum of page 140 however is much more complicated than this, for it shows a 'hyperfine structure' ranging over a magnetic field variation of 20 oersteds. This indicates that the energy level of the unpaired electron of the phenoxy radical is being perturbed by local magnetic fields due to the hydrogen nuclei within the organic radical. If an unpaired electron is affected by the magnetic field of one par-ticular hydrogen nucleus only then, on account of quantized energy coupling, the E.S.R. spectrum should split into a doublet, and if the electron is symmetrically oriented with reference to a pair of hydrogen nuclei then the spectrum should show a triplet of equally spaced lines of relative intensities $= 1:2:1$.

The diagram shows that the main hyperfine splitting of the E.S.R. spectrum of the phenoxy radical is that of a doublet: clearly this can be associated with the canonical structure (XIV, b) in which the odd electron is in the locality of the *para* C—H bond. Superimposed on this however is a triplet splitting which can be associated with the symmetrical pair of *ortho* C—H bonds in structure (XIV, c), but a further small splitting of each of these lines into triplets is also detect-able and this must necessarily be associated with the *meta* C—H bonds.

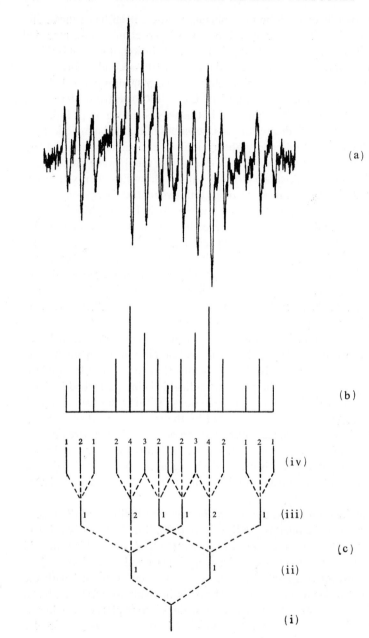

Now in E.S.R. spectra the magnitudes of the magnetic field changes between associated resonance lines (i.e. doublets, triplets, etc.) are a measure of the degree to which an unpaired electron can be regarded mathematically as being localized in a particular region in a radical, as represented by the contributing canonical structures (XIV, a, b, c) which may be drawn out for it, and wave mechanics calculations, which are still somewhat tentative in respect to their theoretical basis, indicate, from the E.S.R. spectrum of the phenoxy radical, that about 40% of the 'odd electron density' should be associated with the *para* canonical structure (XIV, b) and about 25% with the *ortho* structure (XIV, c).

In this way, therefore, we are beginning to gain new insight into the true electronic structures of free radicals and there is hope that theorists may soon be able to predict, from these E.S.R. measurements, the relative extents to which mesomeric aryloxy and arylamino radicals should undergo chemical reactions (a) at their oxygen atoms, (b) at the *para* carbon atoms, and (c) at *ortho* carbon atoms. For instance, it has been found that aryloxy radicals containing electron-attracting substituent groups (e.g. the radical from *p*-hydroxybenzaldehyde) have a greater percentage of the total 'electron spin density' associated with the aromatic ring than is the case for the simple phenoxy radical; thus they have a lower electron density in the region of the oxygen atom of the phenoxy group. Now the oxidation of a phenoxide anion to a phenoxy radical involves the abstraction of an electron,

4. $\qquad (:O{-}C_6H_4{-}R)^- \longrightarrow (\cdot O{-}C_6H_4{-}R) + e$

and this should be less easy the more the group R pulls electrons towards it. It is in fact decidedly more difficult to oxidize such phenols to radicals than it is to oxidize phenol itself. *p*-Chlorophenol, for instance, cannot be oxidized by alkaline ferricyanide but requires an oxidant of higher redox potential. Conversely, alkyl groups decrease the 'electron spin density' associated with the aromatic ring and alkylated phenols are more easily oxidized to radicals than is phenol

---

(a) E.S.R. Spectrum of the Phenoxy Radical, $\cdot O{-}C_6H_5\cdot$
(b) Reconstruction spectrum based on coupling constants obtained from (a)
(c) The origin of the lines in the spectrum: (i) is the free electronic level, (ii) shows the interaction with one *para*-hydrogen, (iii) interaction with two *ortho*-hydrogens, and (iv) interaction with two *meta*-hydrogens.

itself. Technical chemists have for several years known that alkylated phenols are more potent inhibitors of autoxidations than is phenol.

Ultimately, complex mixtures result from all homolytic oxidations of phenols or aromatic amines. The simplest products that can be isolated from monohydric phenols are radical dimers produced by coupling either through oxygen or through carbon atoms; diaryl peroxides, Ar—O—O—Ar, however are not stable reaction products. Coupling through conjugated side-chains can also occur, whilst again alkyl substituents can evidently be lost from many phenols at some late stage of the oxidation process. Typical examples of these coupling reactions are given below.

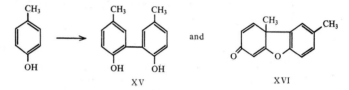

The dual course of the oxidation of *para*-cresol shows clearly the mesomeric nature of the aryloxy radical involved. The diphenol (XV) is obviously formed by coupling at two *ortho* carbon atoms, whilst Pummerer's ketone (XVI) can be formed by coupling one *ortho* carbon atom to one *para* carbon atom and subsequently forming an ether linkage by a heterolytic reaction (see Barton, Deflorin and Edwards, *J. Chem. Soc.* 1956, 530, for details of the probable reaction sequence). This ketone is a particularly interesting dimer, for some important natural plant products have structures of a similar type.

The dimer (XVII) from 1-methyl-2-naphthol again is a keto-ether, but here units of the type of (XIV, a) and (XIV, c) have combined together.

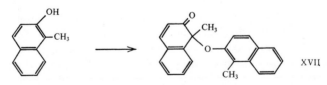

The course of oxidation of iso-eugenol (XVIII) to the heterocyclic compound (XIX) is of particular biological interest in connection with the chemistry of plant products related to lignin. Here we see that the mesomeric structure of the radical from (XVIII) must have a high degree of electron localization at the conjugated β-position in the unsaturated side-chain.

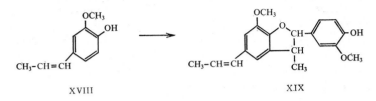

XVIII   XIX

Further stages of the oxidation of the diphenol (XV) have not yet been elucidated, but the *para*-diphenol (XX) formed from 2,6-xylenol can easily be oxidized further to a stable, red diphenoquinone (XXI). The formation of coloured products such as this is an undesirable eventuality with several phenols that otherwise would be good technical anti-oxidants.

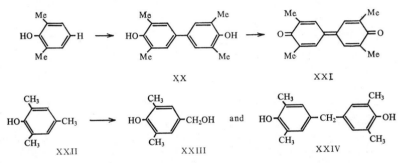

XX   XXI

XXII   XXIII   XXIV

From mesitol (XXII) the simplest products that have been isolated are (XXIII) in which one of the methyl groups has been oxidized, by a route which is indicated below (p. 144), and (XXIV) in which one of the *para*-methyl groups has been lost.

In the case of 4-methyl-2,6-ditertiarybutyl phenol, which is a regularly used additive to petroleum and lubricating oils, two oxidation courses have been established. With tertiary butyl hydroperoxide as the oxidant, so that peroxide radicals are present in high concentration, the dienone (XXVI) results and this can be degraded to the simple benzoquinone (XXVIX) in which the methyl group has been lost.

In contrast, with alkaline ferricyanide as the oxidant, or under conditions of low peroxide radical concentration designed to resemble that corresponding to that holding in an autoxidizing hydrocarbon, the stilbene-quinone (XXX) is finally obtained. This quinone is

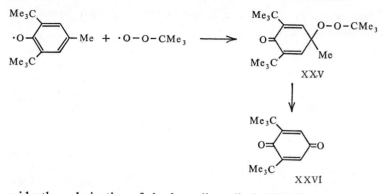

evidently a derivative of the benzylic radical (XXIX) and there is evidence that this radical is formed by hydrogen transfer between the aryloxy radical (XXV) and the original phenol (XXVIII).

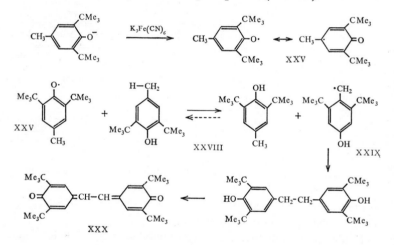

From recent E.S.R. studies it has been found that aryloxy radicals and phenols can equilibrate, by hydrogen transfer

5. $R_1—C_6H_4—O\cdot + H—O—C_6H_4—R_2 \rightleftharpoons$
$$R_1—C_6H_4—O—H + \cdot O—C_6H_4—R_2$$

so that the more stable radical preponderates. A similar equilibration occurs between aryloxy radicals and aromatic amines or oximes.

Since free aryloxy radicals can, in part, behave as radicals of trivalent carbon they are able to combine directly with free radicals of other types. For instance it has been shown that the 2,4,6-tri-tertiarybutyl-phenoxy radical (XXXI), which is a purplish blue sub-stance of long free lifetime, easily combines with atmospheric oxygen to give the dienone peroxide (XXXII) which can break homolytically, in the way shown below, to the original phenol and 2,6-ditertiary-benzoquinone (XXVII), one of the tertiary butyl groups being elimi-nated as isobutene.

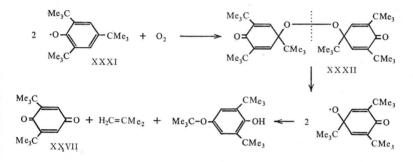

These reactions between aromatic free radicals and atmospheric oxygen have, until recently, received little consideration, but clearly they should be taken into account in relation to the kinetic analysis of autoxidation processes. Reactions of this type may also have to be taken into account in the elucidation of the nature of products of phenol oxidation in solution, for it has seldom been recognized that dissolved air might influence the course of the reactions that are occurring.

One recent study (Hewgill, Stone and Waters, in press) of atmos-pheric oxidation merits note, since it provides an example of the way in which electron spin resonance study of free radicals has been applied to a mechanistic problem. This is the case of the oxidation of catechol (XXXIII) which, when in alkaline solution, soon turns dark on exposure to the air and yields a complex mixture formerly thought to consist of decomposition products of *ortho*-benzoquinone (see p. 146). Actually the anion of catechol first oxidizes to the mesomeric radical (XXXIV) which can be identified by characteristic features of the hyperfine structure of its E.S.R. spectrum. Soon, however, this spectrum decreases in intensity as in its place a second E.S.R. spectrum, which can be identified as that of the radical (XXXIX), appears. This second radical has a life-time of several hours, but

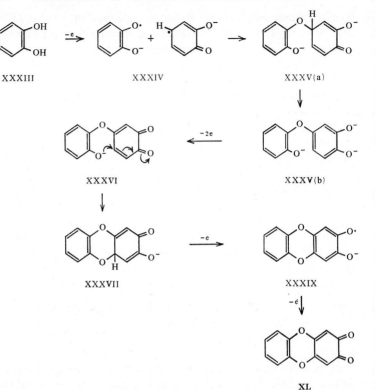

XL

eventually it oxidizes to the stable yellow quinone (XL) which can be isolated from the reaction mixture.

The dimer (XXXV) of the initial semiquinone (XXXIV) is both a phenol ether and an *ortho*-quinol. Evidently it must oxidize to the quinone (XXXVI) too rapidly for the detection of the E.S.R. spectrum of any radical intermediate. Ring closure of the quinone (XXXVI) to (XXXVII) is a typical heterolytic reaction of a phenol with a dienone or a quinone, but the oxidation of (XXXVII) which could also be written as *ortho*-quinol must evidently be a one-electron removal process since the radical (XXXIX) has been so clearly identified. The heterolytic stage whereby (XXXVI) gives (XXXVII) is similar to the oxide ring closure step involved in the formation of Pummerer's ketone (XVI, p. 142).

When alkaline solutions of *p*-benzoquinol are allowed to stand in open vessels they soon darken and then can be shown to contain

p-benzosemiquinone, which has a very simple E.S.R. spectrum. So, in both the *ortho* and the *para* series, the anions of dihydric phenols must be able to give up one electron to oxygen, i.e.

6. $(:O-C_6H_4-O:) + O_2 \longrightarrow (:O-C_6H_4-O\cdot) + (\cdot O-O:)^-$

Many features of the homolytic oxidation of phenols are still unsolved. For instance the oxidation of any monohydric phenol by alkaline ferricyanide, or a similar reagent, usually produces far more polymeric than dimeric material and it is not yet clear why this polymer should so easily be formed. The polymers often appear to have chains of aromatic nuclei linked through oxygen and clearly are not formed by the stepwise oxidation of the dimeric molecules instanced above. In fact trimers are formed from many phenols, e.g. p-cresol in surprisingly good yield. Radical addition to phenol molecules, or phenolic anions has been suggested tentatively and the following scheme, due to Staffin and Price (*J.A.C.S.* 1960, **82**, 3632), shows how polymerization might be effected by a combination of homolytic and heterolytic reactions.

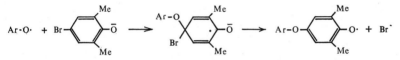

Again *ortho* dihydric phenols are remarkably abundant in nature and these seem to be formed from monohydric phenols by the action of the enzyme *tyrosinase*. To a certain extent this type of oxidation can be simulated by using free oxygen in the presence of an amine and a trace of a copper salt and indeed tyrosinase contains copper as a trace metal component. Quite different oxidations of phenols are effected by other enzymes, and, of these, oxidations of phenols with hydrogen peroxide in the presence of *peroxidase* show many similarities with oxidations of phenols by Fenton's reagent, though several differentiating features have been noted. These may perhaps be due to the different reactivities of $\cdot$OH and $\cdot$O—OH radicals or again to the intervention of free oxygen.

In contrast to these complications, the inorganic radical-ion $\cdot$O—N(SO$_3$K)$_2$, known as Frémy's salt, efficiently oxidizes monohydric phenols to quinones in dilute aqueous alkali. It was introduced as a selective oxidant in 1953 by H. J. Teuber. This oxidation has quite a simple reaction mechanism, for the radical-ion would be expected to combine rapidly with an aryloxy radical and a simple heterolytic elimination would follow.

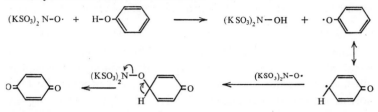

The homolytic oxidation of aromatic amines is undoubtedly similar, in its general mechanism, to the oxidation of phenols but it is much more complicated. Firstly, such oxidations may lead to dehydrogenation or even to the removal of alkyl substituents attached to nitrogen atoms, and secondly the combination of aromatic nitrogen radicals tends to give rise to heterocyclic nitrogen ring systems. From mono-amines dimeric products can be obtained both by C—C and C—N coupling. Further oxidation of the latter type of compound gives rise to radical cations of the type of the 'Würster salts', of which (XLI) is the simplest representative.

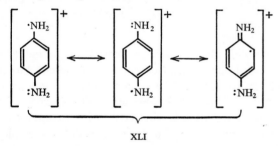

XLI

Once a *para* diamine has been oxidized to a quinon-imine (XLII) the latter rapidly couples heterolytically with molecules of any available amine, and the aromatic product (e.g. XLII) can easily be oxidized to a complex dyestuff.

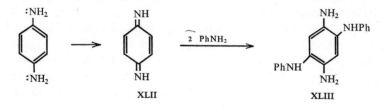

XLII   XLIII

The diamino-phenazine (XLVI) has been identified as an oxidation product of *ortho*-phenylene-diamine (XLIV) and this oxidation, usually represented as passing through the quinon-imine (XLV), is an exact parallel of the oxidation of catechol which has been described on page. 146.

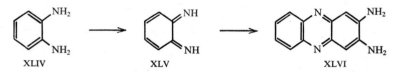

In fact nearly all atomatic amines, upon oxidation, are converted to mixtures of red, purple or blue dyestuffs of the induline or safranine groups and these are essentially phenazine derivatives. W. H. Perkin's original synthetic dye *mauveine*, produced by oxidation of crude aniline, was a mixture of compounds of this general type. Such dyestuffs, though brilliant in tincture, are seldom used today since they fade far too rapidly on exposure to sunlight.

As yet, far too little is known of the organic chemistry of free radicals of nitrogen for mention of detailed reaction mechanisms for the oxidations of aromatic amines to be included in this book. Apposite suggestions however have been put forward by B. C. Saunders (*J. Chem. Soc.* 1951, 2113) who has studied the coloured products of peroxidase oxidation of several aromatic amines and has compared them with products obtained by the use of Fenton's reagent.

General reading references

LOUDON, J. D., 'Developments in the Hydroxylation of Phenols', in *Progress in Organic Chemistry*, Vol. 5. Butterworths, London, 1961.

WATERS, W. A., 'Homolytic Oxidation Processes', in *Progress in Organic Chemistry*, Vol. 5. Butterworths, London, 1961

Index

(References to main discussions are given in bold type).